Testing for Combat

Testing for Combat

Captain Eric Brown

Airlife

England

First published in the UK in 1994
by Airlife Publishing Ltd

British Library Cataloguing in Publication Data
  A catalogue record for this book
  is available from the British Library

ISBN 1 85310 319 5

Printed by **WBC**, Bridgend, Mid Glam.

Airlife Publishing Ltd
101 Longden Road, Shrewsbury SY3 9EB

Contents

Foreword

My previous books have tended to concentrate on the more exotic of the 487 basic types of aircraft I have flown. However, I have obviously been involved in testing or just flying some 'ordinary' aircraft which have turned out to be not so ordinary as they appeared, because of some unusual features they have displayed, or by virtue of some non-standard equipment for which they have acted as flying test beds.

A leading aviation magazine once called me 'the worst insurance risk in a high risk profession' when I commanded Aero-dynamics Flight at the Royal Aircraft Establishment, Farnborough. Be that as it may, a test pilot also has many moments of absorbing interest or even sheer flying pleasure, and I have sought to capture some of these in this book.

I enjoy writing about aviation, but even more I enjoy the hundreds of letters my books have generated from readers worldwide. This book is therefore a tribute to these aviation buffs for the interest they have shown and the contributions they have made to expanding my knowledge.

Eric M. Brown

Chapter 1
Arado Ar 240

On 10th September 1945 I was despatched by the Royal Aircraft Establishment (RAE) in my trusty Bell Airacobra runabout to seek out an Arado Ar 240, which was reported to be lying intact on an airfield in southern Holland. After a vain search at six airfields I spent the night at Eindhoven, where an intelligence officer gave me a lead which I followed up next day, and flew to Merville in northern France. There, tucked away in a hangar, was this rare aircraft, which the few Free French Air Force officers on the airfield told me had been kept serviceable by Germans in the prisoner of war cage on the airfield perimeter. At my request three Luftwaffe maintenance men were herded over to the hangar and set to work on the Arado while I sat in the cockpit familiarising myself with the layout, which was fairly simple to understand with the standardised German gauge markings and colour coding.

I had already had an intelligence briefing in the UK on the Ar 240 and its interesting development history. It was originally designed to a German Air Ministry specification for a fast twin-engined multi-purpose aircraft fitted with two of the newly developed FA 13 systems of remotely controlled armament. The prototype first flew on 10th May 1940, but by that time the FA 13 system had been delayed because of development problems. The Ar 240 was a mid-wing monoplane powered by two 1,075 hp Daimler-Benz DBY 601A engines with annular radiators, and carried a crew of two in a pressurised cabin. The first two prototypes had such appalling instability that a drastic redesign was necessary.

The third prototype had the fuselage length increased by just over 4 ft, and the tail-mounted airbrake replaced by a short cone with auxiliary fins. The pressurised cabin was also moved to the extreme nose of the aircraft, and two FA 13 barbettes were mounted either side of the fuselage, aft of the cockpit. The first flight was made in April 1941, but the handling problems persisted even though new ailerons were fitted. In spite of this, the aircraft made several reconnaissance flights over Britain with impunity because of its high speed.

The fourth prototype reverted to the tail-mounted dive brake, and was powered by two 1,750 hp DB 603A engines, a tremendous power increase over its predecessors. Eight pre-production aircraft were then built before the whole Ar 240 programme was cancelled in December 1942. These eight models had differing engine and armament installations in an attempt to find the right operational mixture, and two even had a new wing of increased span and improved profile and were powered by 1,900 hp DB 603G engines.

The model which I found in France was powered by 1,473 hp DB 605A engines with provision for water-methanol injection. It had been stripped of its armament, but had previously been fitted with a pair of MG 17 machine guns, and four MG 81 machine-guns in each of two FA 13 barbettes. From information gleaned from the German POWs it seems likely that this particular aircraft had flown reconnaissance missions over Great Britain.

When the Ar 240 was wheeled out of the hangar I was struck by its angular appearance. The wings, fuselage, and tail unit all seemed to be straight-edged, with very few curves to be seen. The engines

The Ar 240A-02 in service near Petsamo in northern Finland during the winter of 1942/43.

looked very large, the airscrew spinners being level with the nose of the cockpit and well ahead of the wing leading edge, while the nacelles protruded well aft of the trailing edge. I had the feeling that, if this aeroplane was as fast as it was reputed to be, then brute engine force must be the answer. Its span of 43 ft 9 in almost equalled its length of 42 ft 0⅓ in, and it had a height of 12 ft 11½ in. Empty weight was 15,323 lb and loaded weight 19,624 lb. Two crew were carried, seated back-to-back.

Much to my surprise the engines started easily in spite of their long lay-off, and sounded very healthy, although I gave them a very thorough run-up and checked the associated gauges carefully. The cockpit layout was neat and the instruments were quite logically arranged, while the view was good all around except downwards on either side, where the engines interfered.

Take-off was quite long, even with using 20 degrees of flap, and the initial climb rate was just over 2,000 ft/min. Longitudinal stability was poor, lateral stability neutral, and directional stability positive. The rate of climb fell off very little as I climbed to 20,000 ft, where I levelled out and settled into the cruise at what I calculated was a true airspeed of 360 mph.

In the cruise the aeroplane could not be flown hands-off because it diverged quickly both longitudinally and laterally, and would be tiring to fly for a long time. An autopilot was fitted, although not serviceable in my case, but I believe it would have been essential for instrument flying in bad weather. On opening up to full power I estimated that after 3 min I was hitting an impressive true airspeed of 390 mph, but it was obvious that the Ar 240 was a poor weapons platform. The harmony of control was terrible, with heavy ailerons, light elevators, and moderately light rudders.

The stalling characteristics really showed up the nasty side of this aeroplane. Both the all-up and all-down stalls occurred sharply and almost without warning, except for a twitch on the ailerons before the port wing dropped viciously and the aircraft entered an incipient spin unless rapid corrective action was taken. In steep turns, such as would be taken in evasive action, the aircraft could snap over inverted without any warning if too much 'g' was pulled. The best method of recovery in this case was just to relax on the stick and let the aircraft fall into a vertical dive, but a lot of height was lost before recovery could be effected.

The next Achilles' heel proved to be the asymmetric flight characteristics at slow speed. My tests showed that the maximum speed at which the aircraft could be held straight with one engine out was 160 mph. Below that speed the Ar 240 rapidly entered an uncontrollable spiral dive in the direction of the dead engine.

The limiting diving speed was placarded as 750 km/h (466 mph) and the aircraft accelerated rapidly to this. On opening the tail airbrakes at that speed the most almighty buffet started on the elevators, but fortunately the deceleration was quite rapid and the buffet decreased commensurately.

The recommended approach speed of 225 km/h (140 mph) did not feel comfortable because of the ineffectiveness of the elevators and ailerons at that speed, and touchdown at 120 mph was somewhat tricky because it was not easy to judge the hold-off with such poor longitudinal control. Once the aircraft was firmly on the ground the directional control was reasonable on the run-out, but the brakes, as usual with German aircraft, were totally inadequate, although in this case they might have suffered from the aeroplane's long spell of inactivity. Anyway, I had to swing it on to the grass to get it to stop within the airfield boundary.

My assessment of the Arado Ar 240 is that it was an aircraft of outstanding performance for its class and era, but it could not capitalise on this because of inferior and indeed dangerous handling characteristics. According to German information it had a service ceiling of 34,450 ft and a maximum range of 1,186 miles, so it had great potential as a reconnaissance intruder, and indeed it is claimed that it made such sorties over Great Britain in 1941 and 1944. Be that as it may, there can be little doubt that the Ar 240 was a failure, and indeed some three months after I flew it I was vividly reminded of it when I tested the Messerschmitt Me 410, which had similar handling faults and was likewise a failure.

Considerable mystery surrounded this particular Ar 240. Why was it intact in a hangar in Merville with its German markings obliterated, and even its *Werknummer* (works number) painted over? The three Luftwaffe maintenance men I interrogated said they thought it belonged to the *Sonderaufklärungsstaffel* (special reconnaissance squadron) of the Commander-in-Chief of the Luftwaffe in France, and had been overlooked by the Allied troops in the rapidity of their advance after the invasion of France. My report to the RAE obviously did not whet enough interest in this rare aeroplane to justify negotiating for its removal from the French, and it was left to its fate, whatever that may have been.

Chapter 2
Armstrong Whitworth Whitley

The Whitley heavy night bomber was an outcome of Britain's 1934 rearmament programme, and went into production off the drawing board. It was of mid-wing design, powered by two 795 hp Armstrong Siddeley Tiger IX 14-cylinder air-cooled radial engines with single-speed superchargers, driving three-bladed two-position de Havilland propellers. It first flew on 17th March 1936.

The Whitley was characterised in flight by its marked nose-down attitude, owing to the large angle of incidence of the wing relative to the fuselage in order to keep the landing speed low. Flaps were later added, but too late to alter the wing setting. The first aircraft with a stressed-skin fuselage to go into production for the RAF, it had two manually-operated turrets, in the nose and tail, each with a single Vickers 0.303-in machine-gun. The bomb load of 3,360 lb was carried internally in the fuselage and wings. The wing span was 84 ft, with an empty weight of 14,275 lb, increasing to 21,660 lb when loaded.

My first acquaintance with the Whitley occurred at RAE Farnborough, where one was being used for experiments with a

The Whitley V in its characteristic nose-down flying attitude.

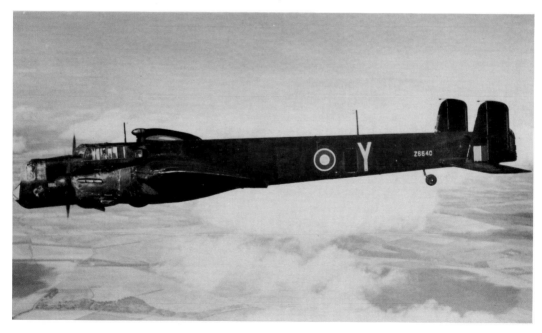

parachute air brake device contained in a box under the aft end of the fuselage. When released, the parachute flew attached to a special tow point, and could act as a dive brake or a landing air brake. Three types of parachute were tried, one of 7 ft diameter, the second of 10 ft and the third of 12 ft.

The smallest parachute was found unsatisfactory in both modes because of insufficient drag, so we proceeded to the largest one. With the 12 ft parachute deployed as a dive brake the Whitley could be dived at an angle of 40 degrees with a maximum speed build-up to only 150 mph. Throughout the dive there was sufficient control to turn the aircraft on to a given target. However, no landings were attempted with the 12 ft parachute as it was considered that its great drag might produce unmanageable difficulties near the ground.

The 10 ft parachute could be dragged without height loss at 2,000 ft, but only with flaps and undercarriage raised. In the light of this it was decided to go ahead with 'chute deployed landings. The tests showed that a low-power landing at 85 mph, giving quite a steep approach, was fully controllable. It was then decided to increase power, reduce speed, and make a flatter approach. Speed was allowed to drop below 80 mph, where with full nose-heavy trim it was necessary to push the control column fully forward, holding a pressure of approximately 45 lb to counteract a large nose-up moment that developed. This action induced the nose to drop and speed to increase slowly, but any opening of the throttles caused the nose to rise again. The quandary was that, if the risk was taken to jettison the parachute at such low altitude, the nose might drop so violently that recovery would be impossible. Fortunately there was just enough height to get the speed up to 85 mph and collide with the runway.

A third landing with parachute deployed was made at low power at 80 mph, and this gave a steep approach angle from which a normal landing could be made. It was

therefore obvious that 80 mph was the cut-off point of controllability in the landing configuration while dragging the 10 ft parachute. This was checked again at 1,500 ft and at any speed below 80 mph a large nose-up pitch occurred every time, so the experiment was terminated as far as landing was concerned.

Obviously these trials were not aimed specifically at the Whitley, which was just a suitable vehicle for the purpose, but it did demonstrate to me the great control forces that can be involved in handling a large aircraft. Actually the main intended use of the landing air-brake parachute was on large troop-carrying or tank-carrying gliders such as the Airspeed Horsa, for which the Whitley V was widely used as a tug.

It will be apparent from the foregoing that the Whitley was a heavy aircraft to fly as far as control forces were concerned, and this was particularly so with regard to lateral control. It was therefore decided in early 1945, when the Whitley's operational days were virtually over, to experiment with the fitting of spring-tab ailerons on a Whitley V to determine their effect on the lateral control.

The Whitley V was fitted with a pair of 1,145 hp Rolls-Royce Merlin X liquid-cooled engines, and otherwise differed from earlier marks in having the rear end of the fuselage extended by 15 inches to give the rear gunner a wider field of fire on the beam. It had modified fins with straight instead of curved leading edges, an increased fuel load, and wing leading edge de-icing equipment.

The aircraft used for the experiment was EB409, and the spring-tab ailerons were to be flown in three different conditions to measure rates of roll at 20 mph intervals from 100 mph to 220 mph. The Whitley had a standard half-wheel control column.

The first condition was with medium spring fitted, with 20 lb preload. In flight the ailerons were much lighter than standard, and full aileron could be applied at all speeds without extensive stick forces being involved. A slight lumpiness was noticeable at the moment of application and seemed to be aggravated with rapidity of stick application, but otherwise the feel of the control was pleasant.

The second set of tests was with the tabs locked. The ailerons were very heavy, and full aileron required a strong physical effort at 180 mph and was virtually an impossibility at 220 mph. In effect, this condition was the same as for aileron control in the standard aircraft.

The third condition was with light spring fitted, with 20 lb preload. The ailerons were incredibly light and felt dangerously capable of causing structural failure. The build-up in stick force with speed was very small indeed. As with the medium spring there was lumpiness at the moment of stick application and a slight build-up of force with increase of aileron angle.

These tests were part of a strenuous effort being made by American, British, and German designers in the latter stages of the Second World War to improve

lateral control both in fighters and bombers. The Germans had shown the way in the Fw 190, which had a superb rate of roll that gave it a vital manoeuvering edge over its contemporaries, and in pursuit of this standard designers were resorting to the use of spring tabs and hydraulic power-boosting. In the case of the bomber the British preference for night bombing had shown a requirement for lighter controls in 'corkscrewing' to evade night fighter attack or searchlight illumination after detection.

The Whitley V was of course only a test bed for any such tests, as it was withdrawn from night bomber operations in the spring of 1942. With a top speed of 230 mph, a maximum weight of 33,500 lb and much heavier defensive armament the Mark V was a considerable improvement on the Mark I, and 1,466 were built. However, the Whitley was a pedestrian aircraft to fly, although one feature endeared it to its crews for night operations, namely good take-off and landing characteristics.

The thick wing section of the Whitley V is clearly shown.

Chapter 3
Armstrong Whitworth Albemarle

The Albemarle's design specification gave it a bad start in life, and one from which it never fully recovered. Originally conceived by the Bristol Aeroplane Company as a twin-engined medium bomber, the design responsibility was transferred to Armstrong Whitworth to build a reconnaissance-bomber to specification B.18/38. This specification called for the aircraft to be built mainly of wood and steel, because officialdom feared that war might bring a shortage of strategic alloys. It also called for wide sub-contracting to firms not employed on strategic war work; and finally the aircraft had to be constructed in road-transportable sub-assemblies.

The Albemarle was a mid-wing cantilever monoplane powered by two 1,590 hp Bristol Hercules XI 14-cylinder sleeve-valve, air-cooled radial engines driving de Havilland three-bladed fully-feathering hydromatic propellers. Fuel was carried in two fuselage tanks and two in the wing centre section, totalling 769 Imperial gallons. A real innovation for an RAF aircraft produced in Britain was the fitting of a tricycle undercarriage.

The standard tricycle-undercarriage Albemarle.

The original armament was a Boulton Paul electrically-operated four-gun turret on top of the fuselage, and a two-gun manually-operated turret underneath. A transparent area at the rear end of the fuselage was to house a fire controller to co-ordinate the defensive fire. A large bomb bay with hydraulically-operated doors extended from just aft of the cockpit to about halfway between the wings and the tail. In the event, the ventral turret and the fire-controller concept were soon dispensed with.

A hairy first flight at Hamble on 20th March 1940 led to an immediate decision to increase the wing span by 10 ft to 77 ft. The length was 59 ft 11 in, and the height 15 ft 7 in. Empty weight was 23,000 lb and maximum 36,500 lb.

The Albemarle's cockpit was very similar to that of its stablemate, the Whitley, and the view ahead was good in spite of the long nose, thanks to the tricycle layout. Take-off was long, but considerably improved by use of one third flap. The single-engine safety speed at normal weight was 125 mph. The climb was very ponderous, but the aircraft exhibited good stability characteristics. In normal flight the controls were heavy, except that the rudders tended to lighten over the last quarter of their travel.

The all-down stall was preceded by slight airframe vibration and marked sink before a wing dropped at 79 mph. A considerable amount of height was lost in recovery unless power was used to give slipstream over the elevators, which were otherwise rather ineffective in this situation.

The Albemarle did not have good single-engine performance, especially as its engines were prone to overheating in this condition. It had a maximum speed in normal flight of 265 mph at 10,500 ft, an appalling service ceiling of 18,000 ft, and a range of 1,300 miles at 170 mph.

In the summer of 1944 a unique Albemarle, V1599, arrived at RAE Farnborough fitted with a long-stroke undercarriage which measured 12 ft long when fully extended and was designed to move backwards as well as upwards under landing loads. For retraction the 24 in long-travel shock absorbers were compressed when the undercarriage was raised.

The object of this experiment was to test the feasibility of flying an aircraft on to a runway in a constant angle of descent, at constant speed and constant power with no flare-out before touchdown. Since this approximated to the Fleet Air Arm deck landing technique used on aircraft carriers, I was given the project.

The tests began by ascertaining the necessary power and elevator trim settings required to set up various rates of descent in the landing condition at 95 mph. The rates of descent were to start at 400 ft/min and be increased by increments of 100 ft/min up to 1,000 ft/min.

The advent of the tricycle undercarriage had simplified the final stage of landing by removing the requirement for the time-honoured 'three-pointer', thereby virtually eliminating the risk of bounce. Also, it made the landing run-out much more directionally stable and permitted greater crosswind limits for operations. However, not even a normal trike will take a high vertical velocity landing without bounce, which can lead to dangerous nosewheel slam, or at worst cause the undercarriage to collapse. A normal landing is made at around 8 ft/sec vertical velocity. With the long-stroke undercarriage fitted to V1599 we were aiming to double that figure.

The tests proceeded normally up to 600 ft/min, but thereafter things began to get increasingly hairy in respect of just sitting tight and waiting for the ever-increasing crunch. By the time we got up to 1,000 ft/min I felt like a kamikaze pilot, but the landing gear behaved magnificently and absorbed its punishment without complaint. These tests were conducted for the Structures and Mechanical Engineering Department at RAE, and led to the development of long-stroke under-carriages for naval aircraft, which during

The Albermarle I

deck-landing often record vertical velocities of 10 to 14 ft/sec.

What of the Albemarle itself? It was really an undistinguished aircraft, which found its operational niche as a glider tug and took part in the invasion of Sicily, the invasion of Normandy, and the airborne assault on Arnhem. A squadron of them were also used as freight carriers by Transport Command.

Ten Albemarles were supplied to the Soviet Union, but little is known of their fate. Although the Soviets may not have been over-excited about the aeroplane itself, they must have welcomed the Hercules engines, which they are believed to have copied.

The overheating problem with the Hercules in the Albemarle led to one aircraft being fitted with Wright Double Cyclone engines, but it came too late to give a new lease of life to an aeroplane whose production run was terminated in December 1944, after 602 had been built.

Although the Albemarle has left barely any imprint on aviation history, V1599 certainly has its own special place in my piloting memories as I recall it squelching into the Farnborough runway with complete impunity.

Chapter 4
Avro Tutor

The Avro 621 two-seat basic trainer was designed in 1929 by the great Roy Chadwick, who later was to design the mighty Lancaster. It was a heavily staggered equal-span biplane, and when I first saw it as a schoolboy it was the star of the famous Alan Cobham 'Circus'. It was probably one of the earliest factors in fanning my burning desire to be a pilot.

The 621 was built by A.V. Roe & Co Ltd virtually as a private enterprise. It was a departure from the almost universal wooden construction of the time, having an all-steel fuselage and wings, with fabric covering. The latter were wire braced and had narrow-chord N-type interplane struts, Handley Page slots, and Frise-type ailerons on the lower mainplane only. It had a large horn-balanced rudder, and a streamline-strutted undercarriage, and was powered by an uncowled 155 hp Armstrong Siddeley Mongoose IIIA 5-cylinder radial engine.

Two batches of the trainer were ordered by the Air Ministry to Specification 3/30, but the majority of production aircraft were powered with a 215 hp Armstrong Siddeley

A Tutor at West Malling in 1938.

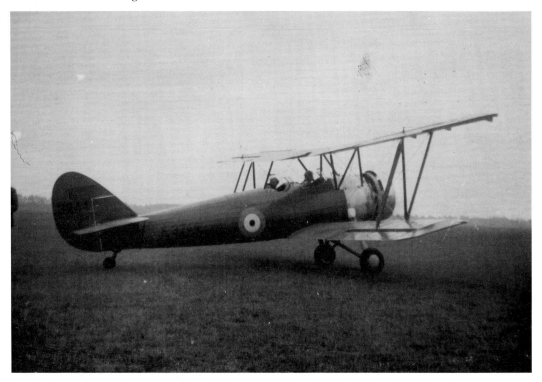

The delightful Tutor trainer.

Lynx IVC, and had an enlarged and rounded rudder.

The 621 was adopted as the standard RAF trainer in June 1932 and named Tutor, a name which was to become synonymous with excellence in that role. Production aircraft for the RAF had the undercarriage moved forward 4½ in, intermediate-pressure wheels with brakes fitted, and with Frise-type ailerons on all four wings as well as duplicated bracing wires.

By 1934 further modifications were introduced – a low drag undercarriage, a Townend ring round the engine, and a tail wheel in place of the original skid. This model was the one I gazed at in awe as it performed delightful formation aerobatics at a prewar Hendon Air Display. It was also the one I was to be fortunate enough to have the opportunity to fly a decade later, thereby realising a boyhood dream.

This relic of the past, Avro Tutor K3424, passed through RAE Farnborough for a few fleeting days in the winter of 1944, and on 14th November I was given a glorious chance to fly this little beauty. It looked in great shape for a piece of history, and I couldn't wait to get it into the air. It spanned 34 ft, was 26 ft 4½ in long and 9 ft 7 in high, and had an empty weight of 1,844 lb and a loaded weight of 2,493 lb.

Each of the spacious open tandem cockpits had little other than a stick, throttle, fuel cock, low-geared trimmer wheel and basic flying instruments. I chose to fly it from the front cockpit. The engine was started by a starter magneto and external hand cranking of the propeller, and once running it had a sound rather like that of an amplified Singer sewing machine. My view ahead was slightly obstructed by the Townend ring but still reasonable for a biplane, but the aircraft had to be swung from side to side for taxying, and in that respect the rudder was very effective and the tailwheel was a considerable help to directional mobility.

The take-off run was surprisingly long, with barely any engine torque to counteract, and the Tutor was climbed at 65 mph, which gave a gentle 900 ft/min. During the climb it was apparent that the aircraft had rather sluggish controls, and that it was directionally stable, with neutral longitudinal and lateral stability.

In the cruise at 1,600 rpm and 90 mph control effectiveness improved, and I was impressed by the harmony of control and the lightness of the ailerons in particular. In aerobatics I found the aeroplane a trifle heavy in the looping plane but very responsive to control inputs, although it needed delicate co-ordination to achieve precision. The Tutor seemed to fly just as well in inverted flight as right way up, and an open cockpit always lends a bit of spice to flying upside down.

Although the aircraft was fitted with a variable-incidence tailplane I found it rather tedious to trim out longitudinal forces because so much winding of the trimmer wheel was required. Its stall at 42 mph was completely innocuous, maybe too much so for a trainer. The spin and recovery were classic, which would imbue confidence in a pupil. The Tutor was a delight to land at 50 mph because of its harmonised controls and low rebound ratio undercarriage, which was very forgiving.

With a top speed of 120 mph, a ceiling of 16,000 ft and a range of 250 miles this was the perfect elementary trainer for its era. It produced for the RAF and Fleet Air Arm a generation of pilots who were to save Britain in its hour of need. Its worth was recognised by the volume of overseas sales, and licences to manufacture it were granted to Denmark and South Africa. A truly splendid aeroplane in every sense of the word.

Chapter 5
Avro York and Lancastrian

The Avro Type 685 was a private venture for a pure transport version of the Lancaster with a redesigned all-metal square-section fuselage having twice the cubic capacity of the original. Designed by Roy Chadwick, it was a high-wing monoplane capable of carrying passengers or freight. The first two prototypes had the Lancaster tail, but all subsequent Yorks, as the type was named, had a third central fin to compensate for increased fuselage side area forward of the centre of gravity. Although it had the same span as the Lancaster it was longer and lower, with a length of 78 ft 6 in and a height of 16 ft 6 in.

The York was powered by four 1,280 hp Rolls-Royce Merlin 22 12-cylinder Vee liquid-cooled engines driving three-bladed constant-speed fully-feathering airscrews. It had the usual six Lancaster wing fuel tanks, but the high-wing layout allowed an extra tank in the centre section. The empty weight was 42,040 lb and maximum weight 68,000 lb.

Taxying the aircraft for my first flight in

The Avro York, seen here in Skyways livery at Bovingdon in 1952, bridged the gap between wartime military transport and post-war commercial airliners.

The Lancastrian 3, in BSAA livery at Heathrow in 1946, did not display the thoroughbred characteristics of its parent Lancaster.

the type, on 9th October 1944, revealed a few points of criticism. Firstly, I found the throttle layout very bad indeed, for besides being in an awkward position overhead, the two outboard levers were so far apart that I could not span them both with the fingers of one hand. The Lancaster type of throttle levers were much better, as the long outboard handles curved in over the shorter inboard ones, thus giving a compact hand grip.

The pilot's position in the nose of the aircraft placed him so far ahead of the wing and main wheels that it required careful negotiation to steer round the corners of the narrow perimeter tracks of the airfields of that era, as the inclination was to steer the nose of the aeroplane and not the wheels. The view from the captain's seat was superb ahead and to port, but owing to the width of the cockpit nothing could be seen

of the starboard wingtip or the starboard outer engine, so the co-pilot would have to be responsible for clearance of obstacles on the starboard side.

The brakes were poor, and under heavy load conditions definitely hazardous. In crosswinds the deep box-car fuselage presented a large keel surface, which tended to take charge, helped by the inadequate braking provided.

Take-off with a flap setting of 25 degrees gave only a slight tendency to swing left which could easily be held on the rudder alone without any differential throttle handling. With elevator trim set one division tail heavy, the aircraft flew itself off in a three-point attitude. Raising the undercarriage gave a slight nose-up change of trim, and raising the flaps gave a fairly steep nose-down change, but the resultant stick force could be held with one hand while retrimming. The initial climb at 170 mph gave a rate of 1,500 ft/min and showed very good lateral and directional stability, but poor longitudinal stability.

In cruising flight at 230 mph the harmony of control was good and the longitudinal stability had improved significantly. In a dive to 300 mph some left rudder was required and there was a very slight airframe vibration. At that speed the ailerons were very heavy, and the rudders light through a very small working range before heavying up progressively. The elevators were moderately light.

Stalls were carried out at 8,000 ft, and for these tests the pilot's airspeed indicator was connected to an experimental static vent 2 ft ahead of the standard one. The all-up stall was preceded by a very gentle buffet and a slight fore and aft pitching motion. Just on the point of stalling at 99 mph a slight twitch was felt on the ailerons before the wing dropped sharply and the aircraft nosed down into a gentle spiral. The all-down stall was preceded by increased buffet, but with no longitudinal pitching. However, the aileron twitch was more violent and the port wing dropped more sharply at the stall at 82 mph before entering a gentle spiral. Recovery from stalls was normal, although it was noticeable that the port wing could be picked up much sooner on rudder than on aileron.

The asymmetric flying qualities of the York were satisfactory. Cutting the starboard outer engine set up a fairly fast roll to starboard with a slight yaw in the same direction. The loss in speed by the time corrective action was taken was 20 mph. Cutting the port outer gave a similar effect, except that the yaw was more accentuated.

In bumpy weather the aircraft was tiring to fly accurately because of a wallow made up of pitch and yaw, requiring a lot of footwork on the rudder.

The York was one of the easiest aircraft to land that I have ever flown. With a splendid view, and making an engine-assisted approach at 110 mph, it assumed a three-point attitude that required the pilot only to close the throttles to effect a perfect landing. There was no tendency to swing after landing even in a crosswind, probably because of the stabilising effect of the wide-track undercarriage. It had a top speed of 298 mph and a service ceiling of 26,000 ft. Range with 12 passengers was 2,700 miles, and with 56 passengers was 1,000 miles.

The York was built with the purpose of bridging the gap between wartime military transport and post-war commercial airliners, and as such it was the best of the military conversion batch that included the Lancastrian, Whitley, Halton (Halifax conversion), Stirling and Warwick. In making this assessment I am conscious that I flew the York without a co-pilot, and that if I had had such a qualified aircrew member aboard some of my criticisms about ground handling would have disappeared.

It is difficult to believe that a finer aeroplane could be found for conversion than the Lancaster, and yet the Lancastrian, which was a less radical conversion than the York, lost some of the flight characteristics of its parent aircraft.

I flew a C. Mark II Lancastrian, VM729, on 12th April 1946 to check the undesirable flight characteristics quoted in the adverse report by the Handling Squadron of the Central Flying School, RAF Hullavington.

The Lancastrian was much more akin to the Lancaster than the York, being the parent aeroplane with all armament removed and with new nose and tail fairings. However, the CFS report criticised it for having rudder overbalance, an excessively high take-off safety speed and undesirable stalling characteristics.

The aircraft I flew was powered by four 1,280 hp Merlin 24 engines mounted in York Tropical Power Plants, and was at an AUW of 55,000 lb with the centre of gravity approximately 45 in aft of the datum.

There was rudder hunt under normal cruising conditions and undoubted rudder overbalance. At +2 lb boost, 2,650 rpm, I could overbalance the rudder at speeds up to 170 knots after about 4/5 degrees travel, but the force to return the rudder beyond the overbalance point was moderately small. Under conditions of asymmetric power the rudder would not overbalance.

The safety speed on take-off was abnormally high, being 150 knots at +18 lb boost and 140 knots at +14 lb boost, 3,000 rpm and using 20 degrees of flap, to hold the swing from a port outer engine cut. Corrective action had to be taken within 4 secs to prevent a dangerous situation developing.

The 'all-down' stall occurred without any warning with aileron snatch to port and a port wing drop of some 60 degrees. The all-up stall was preceded by a slight fore and aft oscillation and aileron twitch before the aileron snatch to port occurred and the wing dropped about 45 degrees.

The Lancastrian went into service with the RAF as well as with British Overseas Airways Corporation and Trans-Canada Airlines on long-range services across the Atlantic and to Australia. Normally nine passengers and five crew were carried over a range of 3,500 miles, but with 3,174 Imperial gallons of fuel carried in four wing tanks and in fuselage tanks beneath the cabin floor, the most economic speed range was 4,500 miles. Such flights were a gruelling experience for the passengers owing to the extended flying time, engine noise, and bumpy weather at medium altitudes.

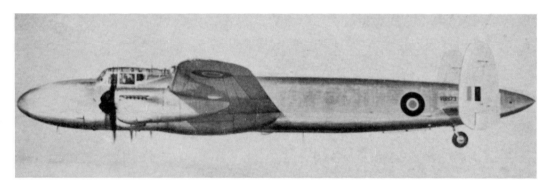

Military versions of the Lancastrian and York.

Chapter 6
Baynes Carrier Wing

In 1941 the aircraft designer L.E. Baynes put forward a proposal for a 100 ft-span wing which could be attached to a medium-sized tank or other armoured fighting vehicle, obviating the requirement for a tail, separate fuselage or under-carriage, as it would use the vehicle's own body and wheels/tracks. Slingsby Sail-planes Ltd was given the task of building a one-third scale piloted model, which was to be fitted with a fuselage and skid under-carriage on a removable two-wheel trolley. The latter would be released on take-off in a fashion similar to that adopted for the

German Messerschmitt 163 rocket inter-ceptor fighter. It had a span of 33 ft 4 in, a length of 11 ft 4 in, a wing area of 160 sq ft, an empty weight of 763 lb and a loaded weight (with ballast) of 963 lb.

This aircraft, RA809, made it first flight in the hands of the well-known glider pilot Flt Lt Robert Kronfeld on 10th August 1943, towed by an Avro Tutor. Shortly after-wards it was handed over to RAE Farn-borough.

I first flew RA809, towed by a Miles Master II, on 22nd February 1945. For take-off the flaps were locked up and the aircraft

The 1/3 scale model of the Baynes Carrier Wing.

remained on the trolley with the control wheel held central until sufficient speed was attained for it to become unstuck by itself, avoiding any temptation to haul the glider off.

Once airborne, the glider was climbed quickly through the tug's slipstream to take up a position above the tug. Towing speed was 110 mph, and at this speed the elevators were extremely sensitive; if elbow rests had not been provided it would have been rather tiring to handle. The ailerons and rudders were somewhat ineffective, with an appreciable lag between application and effect.

After casting off from the tug I set up a glide speed of 70 mph, and it was noticeable that in any bumpy air there was a tendency to Dutch roll, but there was no impression of any instability. The flaps could be lowered at 70 mph and the speed reduced to 60 mph, and they were effective in controlling the glide path.

For landing I learned to set up an approach path at 70 mph with a tendency to overshoot, and then lower the flaps on approaching the airfield boundary. Hold-off required a gentle touch to bring about a stall touchdown on the tail end of the landing skid.

This scale model revealed poor harmony of control, with a particular sensitivity fore and aft which coupled with the indifferent view from the cockpit, made the glider a touchy proposition for landing in confined spaces. The thought of a medium tank appended to it makes the mind boggle. It seemed a good idea at the time, but . . .

Chapter 7
Big Brothers

Does a large-scale version of an aeroplane fly as well as the smaller original, or does it lose something to the growth factor? This is a question that is often asked, so let us look at some examples.

Avro Lincoln

The design was started in 1943 of an improved Lancaster for the Pacific War, and anticipated Air Ministry Specification B.14/43, to which it was built. It followed the well-proven Lancaster formula, but had higher-aspect-ratio wings, a lengthened fuselage, a standard Lancaster tail unit with enlarged rudders, a sturdier Dowty undercarriage and more powerful Merlin engines, namely four 1,750 hp Merlin 85s driving Rotol three-bladed propellers and arranged as detachable power units in low-drag armour plated cowlings with annular radiators.

Armament consisted of a Bristol Type 17 Mk II mid-upper turret and Boulton Paul F and D type turrets in the nose and tail, all mounting twin 0.5 in machine-guns. The

The Lincoln B.2, big brother of the Lancaster.

Lincoln II had 2×20 mm cannon in the mid-upper turret, and the nose guns were remotely controlled by the bomb aimer.

With a span of 120 ft the Lincoln was 18 ft wider than the Lancaster, and its loaded weight of 82,000 lb was 14,000 lb heavier than the Lancaster. It carried seven crew and had a range of 2,640 miles with a 14,000 lb bomb load at 214 mph at 20,000 ft, and 4,450 miles with 3,000 lb of bombs.

There is no doubt that the Lincoln, or the Lancaster IV as it was originally called at the time of its first flight on 9th June 1944, was a big aeroplane for its era. It certainly looked big enough to me when I walked round RE254, which I was about to fly on 2nd April 1946. Somehow it did not make my pulse race like it did the first time I saw the Lancaster, and I rather blamed that on the annular engine radiators and the large rudders, which seemed to detract from the aesthetic beauty characteristic of its little brother.

On getting into the cockpit, my first impression was that the aircraft did not seem to have quite as nose-high a ground attitude as the Lancaster, yet the view ahead was worse owing to the longer nose. Certainly the cockpit layout was virtually identical, so I felt at home immediately.

For take-off with one-third flaps down the Lincoln did not need to be trimmed so nose heavy, being neutral at an AUW of 65,000 lb, whereas at the same weight the Lancaster required 4½ divisions of nose-down trim. Even at 82,000 lb the Lincoln required only 2 divisions nose-heavy. The safety speed of the Lancaster at 65,000 lb was 125 mph, but for the Lincoln it was 145 mph at 75,000 lb and 150 mph at 82,000 lb. The climb at 170 mph showed the same flight characteristics as the Lancaster, but the Lincoln had better performance, taking 26½ min to 20,000 ft, compared with 41½ min for the Lancaster.

In cruising flight the controls on the Lincoln had all heavied up slightly compared with its lighter brother, and this was especially noticeable with the ailerons, the inertia of the greater wingspan also giving a lower rate of roll.

The stalling characteristics had changed. The gentle nose-drop of the Lancaster, preceded by slight tail buffeting some 4 mph before the stall, had been replaced in the Lincoln by a heavier tail buffet and a tendency to drop a wing slightly at the stall.

Asymmetric flying was similar in both aircraft, except that in the case of double engine failure on one side the pilot in the Lancaster was left with a very heavy foot load even with full rudder trim, while in the Lincoln most of the foot load could be trimmed out. However, it was not advisable to wind on more than 10 divisions of rudder trim, or mild rudder overbalance could occur.

Landing was similar in both aircraft except that the Lincoln could be landed at slightly lower speed (a mere 5 mph less). The Lincoln also gained in level flight maximum speed by almost 10 mph, but had a lower service ceiling by 2,000 ft.

In 1948 I was invited by Central Bomber Establishment to fly Lincoln II RF498, named *Crusader* and used on pioneering long-range overseas flights, which seemed to suffer from longitudinal instability. I made my flight on 10th January 1948 at RAF Marham, and soon traced the problem to incorrect sequencing of the fuel system, since the aircraft carried two 400-gallon auxiliary fuel tanks in the bomb bay.

In summary, therefore, the Lincoln's handling characteristics suffered slightly because of its size, but it gained slightly in performance because of more advanced technology (wing and engines). Above all it outstripped the Lancaster in pay-load capacity purely as a result of its sheer size.

Although the Lincoln arrived in service just too late for the Pacific War, it equipped 20 bomber squadrons in 1950 and saw action against insurgent groups in Malaya and Kenya.

Short Stirling

The Short S.29 Stirling was the first four-engine bomber to serve in the Royal Air

The Short S.31 half-scale flying model of the Stirling.

Force, being designed to Air Ministry Specification B.12/36, which called for a range and bomb load far in excess of any previously envisaged. Short Brothers had been essentially builders of flying-boats, so for this new venture they decided to build the S.31 piloted half-scale flying model of the Stirling to provide information on the flying qualities to be expected from the full-scale bomber. The two-seat S.31 was a reasonably faithful model of the mighty S.29, and first flew in 1938. I did not fly it until 1943, but it was 1944 before I flew the full-scale Stirling, so this was the best sequence for comparison purposes.

I have already described my flight experiences with the S.31 in a previous book (*Wings of the Weird and Wonderful*, Vol. II), so it was fascinating for me to fly big brother and compare notes. My four-engine flying time was then limited, and the Stirling made an awesome impression on me when I first saw it. It not only looked huge, but stood tall, the actual height being 22 ft 9 in. Certainly in getting into the cockpit it felt a very long way off the ground.

The sweet purr of the Bristol Hercules XVI engines in that Stirling III was certainly very different from the crackle of the little Pobjoy Niagara IVs in the S.31. The view from my lofty perch was good all round, but during taxying it was evident that the aircraft's large keel surface made it very sensitive to side-wind effect. Take-off using one-third flap produced a pronounced swing to starboard during the initial run owing to blanking of the rudder by the fuselage in the tail-down attitude, but this could be comfortably controlled once the tail was raised. With unstick at 105 mph, the safety speed was 135 mph. These same characteristics were exhibited by the S.31.

The climb at 150 mph with the engine

The Short Stirling, Britain's first four-engined bomber.

cowl gills one third open was very laborious, and displayed neutral longitudinal stability. In the cruise at 215 mph the aircraft still showed neutral longitudinal stability, but was stable laterally and directionally. Harmony of control was good, the elevators being slightly heavy and sluggish in initial movement, the ailerons being surprisingly light and quite effective, thanks partly to the relatively restricted wing span of 99 ft 1 in, while the rudder was moderately heavy. The overall effect was an unusually manoeuvrable large aeroplane, but one that required concentration to fly manually on instruments, although there were two pilots to share the load, unlike in the Halifax and Lancaster. In two respects the Stirling had benefited from the S.31; namely it was fitted with a lateral trimmer and a more effective rudder trimmer.

The stalling characteristics of the Stirling were very uncomplicated, with buffeting warning at some 10 mph before the stalls at 110 mph (all up) and 85 mph (all down) at an AUW of 62,000 lb. The S.31 had not given any stall warning, probably because of the minor difference in the wing planform from that of the full-scale S.29.

Landing the Stirling was not easy by day, far less by night. In the airfield circuit, speed was reduced to 145 mph and flaps lowered one third, followed by the undercarriage before turning on to finals, when the large Gouge-type trailing-edge flaps were fully lowered and the resultant nose-up trim change was trimmed out. The speed was then stabilised on the approach at 110 mph, during which the controls had a sloppy feel. This was particularly evident on the elevators when a large change of attitude was required for hold-off. On the landing run there was a decided tendency to swing, which was not helped by the blanked rudder and the bad position of the wheel-brakes lever on the left of the throttle box. Altogether an adrenalin-pumping operation, which was not fully reflected in the S.31 because of its restricted elevator travel, a point which was corrected in the S.29.

Asymmetric flying on the Stirling involved slightly (one engine out) to moderately (two engines out on one side) heavy rudder foot loads, which could not be trimmed out, so the presence of two pilots was very helpful.

The Stirling has been heavily criticised in official quarters, particularly because of its poor operational ceiling and inability to carry really large bombs, but these restrictions were inherent in the terms of the operational requirement, which limited the wing span and foresaw a bomb load comprising only 500- and 1,000-pounders.

Although the Stirling was in my opinion a pedestrian aeroplane, it might have been slightly more so without the experience derived from the S.31, but the building of such a half-scale model was a doubtfully cost-effective exercise, and not one that has proved popular with other manufacturers.

Vickers Warwick

The Warwick was not intended as a replacement for its little brother, the ubiquitous and successful Wellington medium bomber, but was designed to Air Ministry Specification B.1/35 for a heavy bomber of under 100 ft span so that it could fit into existing RAF hangars. However, the family resemblance was strong and the structural details of the two aircraft had so much in common that the Wellington was virtually a cut-down Warwick, both featuring the Barnes-Wallis lattice-type geodetic form of construction with its high

The Warwick GRIII, troublesome big brother of the placid Wellington.

strength/weight ratio and ability to absorb damage.

The Wellington was characterised by a deep fuselage, tapered wings of high aspect ratio in the mid-wing position and a tall single fin and rudder. It had good stability around all three axes, and acceptable harmony of control with fairly light ailerons, moderately heavy elevators and a heavy rudder. Powered by two 1,000 hp Bristol Pegasus XVIII radial engines, and later by 1,500 hp Bristol Hercules XIs, it had good performance and armament for its era, except that its service ceiling was somewhat limited.

The Warwick started life with a large question mark over which engines would power it – Rolls-Royce Vultures, Napier Sabres, Bristol Centaurus and Pratt & Whitney Double Wasps were all contenders. Production and priority problems ruled out the first two, so the Centaurus powered the operational versions, and the lower-powered Double Wasps the Air Sea Rescue and civil versions.

There were also control problems, as the scaled-up elevators and rudder of the Wellington were found to be too heavy in effect, particularly the rudder for asymmetric flying, when it was subject to aerodynamic overbalance. The overbalance was cured by the addition of a dorsal fin extension, but in spite of a continuous succession of modifications directional instability was still being encountered right up to the end of the Warwick production series. So in February 1945 five GR Mk.Vs were used to try and finally solve the directional problem, and I was invited to fly an additional Mk.I, BV217, at Vickers' experimental establishment at Wisley. This aircraft had been fitted with a spring-tab rudder, and I made two flights on 19th April 1945 to assess its handling characteristics with and without an aerodynamic damper connected.

The spring-tab rudder had a damper acting under pitot pressure to put a load on the rudder with increase in speed, making it less easy to move. The first flight was made with the damper disconnected, and the rudder could only be described as remarkably light for such a heavy aircraft. I had set the rudder trimmer neutral on the ground, and found no occasion to touch it in flight from take-off to landing, for even at the maximum climbing conditions at 135 mph and during a dive to maximum speed of 330 mph the foot load was negligible.

Single-engine flying at maximum climb power produced a very reasonable foot load with full rudder to keep the aircraft straight and level at 5,000 ft. There was no sign of overbalance or any of its symptoms in this condition. I gained the impression that the rudder was dangerously light at high speeds, sufficiently so as to cause structural failure with harsh application or misuse, and that it put the controls much out of harmony at high speeds, when I found the rudder light, the ailerons reasonably light and the elevators heavy.

The second flight was made with the damper connected, and the result showed that the load produced with increase in speed was very well chosen and the effect was altogether pleasant. The rudder was still delightfully light and apparently unaffected at low speeds for climbing and single-engine flight, and there was very little increase in load up to 180 mph in normal cruising flight, but thereafter it began to get noticeably progressively heavier, and had the right feel for such a large aircraft at 330 mph. Harmony of control was also improved with the damper connected.

The Warwick GR Mk V represented the ultimate development of the type, and was eventually cleared to operate at an AUW of 50,000 lb. It had very acceptable handling characteristics, but only after much trial and error, and never quite comparable with those of the Wellington. It also gained slightly in performance, mainly because of its better power/weight ratio, but above all it outstripped the Wellington in payload capacity. In short, the Wellington/ Warwick experience was generally similar

The ubiquitous Vickers Wellington medium bomber.

to that of the Lancaster/Lincoln story, and all really very predictable. Of course, the development of powered controls changed the whole ball game, and size no longer became a barrier to light and effective controls.

Although the Warwick made its first flight on 13th August 1939, it did not get over its development problems in time to make any effective contribution in the Second World War, although it might have been a useful aircraft in the Pacific theatre. In essence it had a short operational life but hardly a gay one.

The towering hulk of the Stirling.

Chapter 8
Blackburn Botha

The Blackburn Botha already had a bad reputation when I first became acquainted with it in 1943. My first impression was that it was not a bad looking aircraft, but its engines looked somewhat small for its size. The elevator projecting aft of the rudder reminded me of the Blackburn Skua.

The Botha was designed to Air Ministry Specification M.15/35, which called for a three-seat, twin-engined reconnaissance bomber with internal stowage for a torpedo. The requirement was then amended in Specification M.10/36, which increased the crew complement to four.

The aircraft appeared in 1938 as a high-wing monoplane with an all-metal monocoque fuselage with flush-riveted stressed-skin covering, and a similar covering on the wings and all fixed tail surfaces. It had fabric-covered, balanced ailerons on the trailing edges of the sharply tapered outer wing sections, which were set at a large dihedral angle, and hydraulically operated split flaps on the trailing edges of the centre section. The rudder and elevator had metal frames and fabric covering, were balanced by a combination of inset hinge and horn balance, and were fitted with trimming tabs. The main undercarriage retracted into the tails of the engine nacelles, while the

The ill-fated Blackburn Botha.

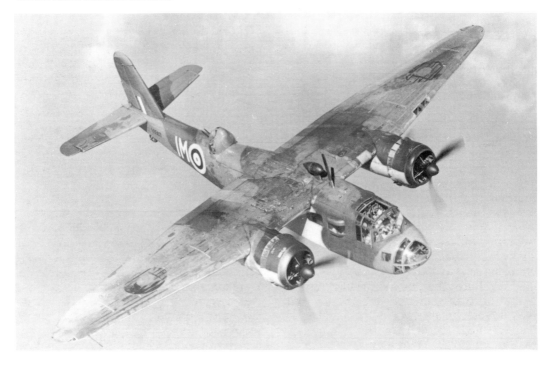

castoring tailwheel was non-retractable.

My Botha was powered by two 930 hp Bristol Perseus XA radial air-cooled sleeve-valve engines driving de Havilland 5/11 Hydromatic three-bladed constant-speed airscrews. The centre section housed the main fuel tanks, two of which contained 143 Imperial gallons, while a third held 132½ Imperial gallons.

The aircraft had a span of 59 ft, a length of 51 ft 0½ in and a height of 14 ft 7½ in. Its empty weight was 12,036 lb, and maximum weight 18,450 lb. Armament consisted of 1×0.303 in Vickers gun forward, fired by the pilot, and 2×0.303 in Lewis guns in an egg-shaped power-operated dorsal turret aft of the wings. One Mk XIII or XIV torpedo or 2,000 lb of bombs could be carried in an internal bay with hydraulically-operated doors which were removed if a torpedo or single 2,000 lb bomb was carried.

The Botha made its first flight on 28th December 1938, powered by two 850 hp Perseus engines, and was obviously underpowered. However, none of the more powerful Taurus engines were available, as they had all been earmarked for Bristol Beauforts, so the production aircraft were fitted with 880 hp Perseus Xs and, later, Perseus XAs.

The cockpit was spacious and well laid out, allowing a very good view forward but a poor view sideways and backwards owing to the engine nacelles. The wireless operator and navigator were housed in the midship cabin, which was entered by a door with a built-in step ladder on the starboard side.

Taxying qualities were poor, owing to indifferent actuation of the throttle levers and the bad directional stability of the aircraft on the ground, although the hydraulic brakes were good. Take-off was shaky at full load, and there was no hope of climb away at any weight in the event of an engine failure. The climb with both engines operating was a modest 985 ft/min, but was adversely affected if the cowl gills were opened. The elevator had a tendency to hunt due to slight buffeting.

In cruising flight the controls were not well harmonised, the elevator being too heavy, the ailerons very light, and the rudder so heavy that it was barely moveable. The elevator hunted slightly but continuously.

The major problem with the Botha was its single-engine flight characteristics. Level flight on one engine at full load was not possible and height was gradually lost, and not so gradually if the cowl gills were opened. The airscrews, of course, could not be fully feathered.

Single-engine practice flying presented a particular hazard. With the necessary rudder trimmer applied, any attempt to open up the dead engine created a very heavy swing because of the strong rudder bias required to hold the aircraft straight, since the rudder was so heavy it could not be held by footload alone. Unless this swing was instantly counteracted by trimmer adjustment, a spin was likely because of the slow speed.

The Botha had a top speed of 220 mph, a service ceiling of 18,400 ft and a range of 1,270 miles. The earlier model with the Perseus X engines was 31 mph faster at 15,000 ft and had a service ceiling of 23,600 ft.

For landing, the Botha had a large nose-up change of trim when the flaps were lowered, and instant elevator trim had to be applied. When settled in the approach, the glide was nice and steep at 85 knots and touchdown was very easy. It was not recommended to make an engine-assisted landing because of the dire consequences of an engine failure on this badly under-powered aeroplane.

The Botha's operational life lasted a mere five months because of its performance and handling shortcomings. As 580 aircraft were built something had to be done with them, and unbelievably the majority were relegated to training while the remainder were assigned to target-towing duties. The decision to use the hopelessly under-powered Botha for training resulted in the inevitable crop of accidents, many fatal, which cast a dark cloud over its reputation.

Chapter 9
Blackburn Firecrest

The Blackburn B-48 Firecrest was designed to meet Specification S.28/43, calling for a Firebrand torpedo-fighter with a redesigned wing and improved pilot's view. The design featured an inverted gull wing with a relatively thin laminar-flow section and a double wing fold (up, and then over and down to meet the fuselage). Four Fowler high-lift flaps with auxiliary flaps on the outer pair were fitted, together with hydraulically-retracting dive brakes above and below the wing.

The pilot was given an unobstructed view over the nose by raising the cockpit and moving it forward so that most of the fuselage fuel tankage was behind it. The downward sweep of the anhedral centre section allowed a short undercarriage stressed to withstand a vertical velocity of 12 ft/sec in carrier landings. It was hydraulically operated, as were the retractable tailwheel and arrester hook. The wing span was 44 ft 11½ in, the folded span was 18 ft, the length 39 ft 3½ in, and the height 14 ft 6 in.

Power was provided by a 2,475 hp Bristol Centaurus 59 18-cylinder sleeve-valve

The first prototype Firecrest.

radial engine with a two-speed super-charger, driving a five-bladed Rotol constant-speed airscrew. Starting was by the Coffman cartridge system. Cooling of the engine was by electrically controlled cowl gills, and was boosted by a multi-blade fan immediately behind the propeller. A total of 236 Imperial gallons of fuel was contained in two wing tanks and two fuselage tanks, fore and aft of the pilot. No armament was installed. The empty weight was 10,513 lb and the maximum weight was 15,280 lb.

Two Firecrest prototypes were built, and the first flight was made on 1st April 1947. The second prototype was not completed to specification, but was modified for research with the power-boosted ailerons being introduced on the Firebrand TF5A. For this reason the dihedral on the outer wing panels was reduced from 9 degrees to 3 degrees. This aircraft, VF172, was delivered to RAE Farnborough for tests in early 1949, and was the only one of the prototypes I flew.

The Servodyne system for the hydraulically powered ailerons had zero feedback to give feel to the pilot, but artificial spring feel was provided. The cockpit controls for the system consisted of a power control lever, an actuator trimmer for altering the spring tension to trim the aircraft laterally when power was on, and a standard electrical aileron trimmer operating a tab on the port aileron to trim the aircraft when power was off. Normally this tab would be set to float up half an inch above the main control surface with the ailerons neutral, so that the aircraft would be approximately in trim in the event of a power failure requiring the pilot to revert to manual control.

When I first saw the Firecrest it reminded me of a rather over-grown Corsair. The Centaurus 59 was certainly the most powerful piston engine I had ever flown behind, and this was reflected in the impressive take-off distance of 430 ft in a 25 knot wind, and an initial climb rate of 2,500 ft/min.

In the air the powered ailerons gave no build-up in operating force with speed, the force being apparently constant throughout the speed range, but there was a moderate build-up in force with stick displacement and rate of application.

A marked lumpiness was felt in the control circuit on initiating any stick movement from the neutral position, leading to a feeling of overbalance in the middle range of control travel. Self-centering of the stick was rapid and positive, but the lateral stick free stability of the aircraft was neutral, and I found it impossible to trim to fly laterally level with hands off, even in calm air. This made the aircraft tiring to fly on instruments in cloud.

The rate of roll at 100 degrees/sec at 210 knots was not very high, and a lighter spring could have been introduced into the circuit to reduce the control displacement force a little. However, the roll rate was acceptable for the aircraft's intended operational role.

After this assessment flight on 11th February 1949, it was decided to test the effect of removing the self-centering preload from the artificial spring feel, so I tried this out on 22nd February 1949.

The first very noticeable change in the characteristics of the aileron control was that all the original lumpiness had disappeared, but it was replaced by an unpleasant feeling of having the stick balanced on a knife edge. Level flight was virtually impossible because the pilot, in attempting to keep the stick truly central, kept overshooting from one side to the other so that the aircraft flew along with a continuous lateral lurching motion. In other respects the feel of the control was more pleasant than in the previous condition because of the lighter application forces.

The stick free lateral instability of the aircraft now made it quite dangerous to fly in cloud, so the minuses really exceeded the pluses in this condition.

In manual reversion the control forces

The second prototype Firecrest.

were very high, and it would just have been possible to carry out a landing in smooth air under such conditions.

Some valuable information on power controls was gleaned from the tests with the Firecrest, and the Firebrand TF5A benefited in that its powered ailerons had a 25% feedback of feel to the pilot and excellent self-centering characteristics. Much of the improvement was due to the proximity of the assister unit to the control column, thus removing friction in the control circuit.

The performance checks on the Firecrest showed a maximum speed of 380 mph at 19,000 ft, a service ceiling of 31,600 ft and a range of 900 miles at 213 mph. The best combat range with a torpedo was 750 miles at 272 mph at 10,000 ft. Although the aircraft's airspeed indicator was graduated in knots, these figures in mph were obtained from special automatic observer instrumentation fitted in the aircraft.

Considering what an abominable naval aircraft the Firebrand was, it seemed incomprehensible that the Naval Staff would seek to perpetuate the concept with the Firecrest, which, with such lineage, was assuredly doomed to failure or, at best, mediocrity. And so it proved to be.

Chapter 10
Boulton Paul Defiant

In the late 1920s it became apparent that open gun positions on military aircraft were becoming impracticable as speeds increased, so in 1932 Boulton Paul was asked to provide an air shield for the front defensive position of the Side-strand bomber. It was soon obvious that an alternative solution had to be found, and a totally enclosed gun turret was proposed. On trials it was a great success, increasing hits per rounds fired on a target by almost 170 per cent compared with those registered by an exposed Vickers gun.

The Air Ministry now saw the possibilities for a turreted two-seat day and night fighter, and issued Specification F.9/35. Boulton Paul's submission closely resembled a turreted Hurricane, and thus found favour with the Air Ministry as it was likely to be operated in conjunction with Hurricanes.

The prototype Defiant first flew on 11th August 1937, with ballast in place of the turret. Delays now started to set in while design changes were made, the turret was put through firing trials, and a later mark of Merlin engine was installed. As a result the first production aircraft did not fly until

The Defiant turreted fighter shows its resemblance to the Hurricane.

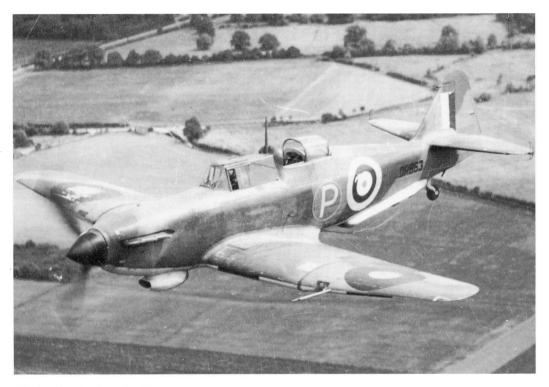

The Defiant in the role of target tug.

30th July 1938, and the type finally entered operational service on 8th December 1939.

The Defiant was a low-wing monoplane with a span of 39 ft 4 in, a length of 35 ft 4 in, and a height of 14 ft 5 in. Its maximum all-up weight was 8,350 lb. Of all-metal construction except for fabric covering on the elevators and rudder, which were horn-balanced, it was fitted with a wide-track retractable undercarriage and a fixed tailwheel.

The Defiant I was powered by a 1,030 hp Rolls-Royce Merlin III 12-cylinder Vee liquid-cooled engine driving a three-bladed de Havilland constant-speed airscrew. The Defiant II had the more powerful 1,280 hp Merlin XX driving a Rotol propeller. Both engine models had a two-speed supercharger. Self-sealing fuel tanks with a total capacity of 159 Imperial gallons were located in the wings. The armament comprised 4×0.303-in Browning machine-guns in a Boulton Paul turret, with 600 rounds per gun. The Defiant II had an increased length of 35 ft 10 in and increased rudder area. Its empty weight was 6,282 lb and maximum take-off weight was 8,600 lb.

The concept of the Defiant as a day fighter was based on operating it in company with Hurricanes to attack unescorted bombers, but the Germans were not so obliging, and although their fighter escorts got a nasty surprise on first encountering the Defiant, this instant success was short-lived once the enemy had sized up the limitations of the turret's field of fire and realised that the new fighter had no forward-firing armament. Inevitably, therefore, the Defiant was assigned to night fighter duties only by the end of August 1940.

To improve its effectiveness in the night role a simple Airborne Interception radar was fitted to Defiants during 1941, and the fuel capacity was increased by 55 Imperial gallons by the addition of a small tank in each wing outer section. These changes increased the maximum weight of the Mk.I to 8,600 lb and of the Mk.II to 8,680 lb. In fact, for its time the Defiant was quite a successful night fighter.

The Defiant's cockpit was quite roomy and well laid out, but the view ahead was not good on the ground. An interesting feature was that the control column was mounted on the pilot's adjustable seat frame, so that its relative position was constant whatever the position of the seat.

The nose of the aircraft had to be swung from side to side during taxying to allow a view ahead, and this had to be done on the brakes because the rudder had little effect. In a crosswind there was no particular weathercocking tendency, and the aircraft felt stable with its wide-track under-carriage.

For take-off the aircraft could be held on the brakes up to full power. With 30 degrees of flap the run was reasonably short, with only a mild tendency to swing. Raising the wheels and flaps gave only a slight nose-up change of trim. The rate of climb was initially about 2,000 ft/min, and the Defiant exhibited good stability characteristics, very suitable for a night fighter. In cruising flight this positive stability was accompanied by good harmony of the controls, which were all moderately light and effective, though not up to the standard of the Hurricane.

There was no noticeable difference in handling characteristics between the Mk.I and Mk.II, but there was a slight improvement in performance with the later model, which had a maximum speed of 315 mph at 16,500 ft and a range of 550 miles at 260 mph.

When the Defiant's operational days were numbered it was decided to build a number for target-towing. This role involved replacing the turret with a rear-facing observer's position and a drogue winch. Indeed, the Defiant's reputation for

stable handling made it a popular choice as a test bed for a wide range of aerial equipment experiments, and I was involved in two of these at RAE Farnborough in the summer of 1946, using Defiant TT.Mk.I DR895, a converted Defiant II.

In 1943 Boulton Paul began to take an interest in naval carrier aviation, and proposed design studies P.103 for a single-seat fighter and P.105 for a two-seat attack aircraft to be operated from carriers. A feature of the P.103 design was a long-stroke undercarriage, and it was intended to fit this to DR895 and carry out deck-landing trials. I was therefore asked to make an assessment of this aircraft's fitness for deck-landing.

In the main, this assessment involved checking the stalling characteristics and then carrying out low-speed powered approaches and landings, since the rest of the Defiant's handling qualities were already well known to me. The all-up stall occurred at 93 mph with very little warning other than a negligible amount of aileron twitching. At the stall the port wing dropped quite smartly to 30 degrees. The all-down stall at 81 mph displayed similar characteristics, except that the starboard wing dropped more gently to 30 degrees. With sufficient power on to simulate the deck-landing condition, the all-down stall occurred at 79 mph without any warning, and the port wing dropped sharply to 30 degrees.

A series of powered approaches at 90 mph showed that the ailerons and elevators were very light and effective, while the rudder was also very light but a little less effective although good enough to cope adequately with the swing set up by full power application, such as in the baulked landing case. The touchdown could be made easily in a three-point attitude provided power was not cut too early. There was no tendency to swing during the quite short landing run.

In the event, no carrier trials were ever carried out, although I passed the aircraft fit to do so in spite of its rather undesirable stall characteristics. However, the long-stroke undercarriage was fitted and proved successful, and indeed this type was eventually fitted to the Hawker Sea Fury.

The other experiment in which I took part was testing the functioning and effect of electrically-operated automatic elevator trim tabs fitted to DR895. The experimental system comprised: **1** a selector lever, whereby the electrical trimming circuit or the manual circuit working off the ordinary hand trimmer wheel could be chosen; **2** a six-position rheostat for pre-selecting the rate at which the trimmer was wound on in the nose-heavy direction; **3** a similar rheostat for the tail-heavy direction; **4** a control button on the stick for trimming the aircraft nose-heavy; **5** a button for trimming tail-heavy; and **6** a master control button on the stick for trimming out any stick force applied in either vertical direction. In actual practice the pilot would be provided merely with item 6 and possibly item 1.

The tests showed that rate 3 or 4 would be ideal for a fighter, giving a rate slightly faster than the rate of electrical operation on the elevator trimmer in the Focke-Wulf Fw 190. For a bomber rate 6 would be best, as in heavy aircraft the control forces build up rapidly. This seems a pretty simple solution to arrive at, but in the process I made a good attempt to demolish the Defiant when using rate 1 to pull out of a dive at the limiting speed of 360 mph, but it was a rugged aeroplane, and an excellent choice as a flying test bed.

Automatic trim tabs of this type actually appeared on the aviation scene too late for widespread adoption, as hydraulic power assisted controls were already coming into service for aileron and rudder control, and were being developed for elevator control.

The Defiant will never be remembered as a great operational aeroplane, but it deserves to be remembered as an aircraft with almost no flying vices.

Chapter 11
Bristol Beaufighter II

The Beaufighter was a Private Venture design conceived in October 1938 as a 'Beaufort Fighter' by incorporating about 75 per cent of the Beaufort torpedo-bomber, the only entirely new components being the main fuselage and engine mountings. Metal was actually cut for the new fighter before the Air Ministry caught up and issued Specification F.17/39 to cover the work.

The Air Ministry then got ahead of the game by ordering 300 aircraft a fortnight before the prototype Beaufighter flew on 17th July 1939. Four development aircraft were built, and the first delivery of a production Beaufighter took place on 27th July 1940. However, the Bristol Hercules radial engines were in short supply, so the Rolls-Royce Merlin XX was chosen as an alternative powerplant. The version with two 1280 hp Merlin XXs became the Beaufighter II.

On first seeing the Beaufighter I was struck by its look of pugnacity and the impression of ruggedness it conveyed, but I knew it had earned a reputation for being

The Hercules radial-engined Beaufighter.

The Merlin-engined Beaufighter II F.

lethal in the event of an engine failure on take-off owing to its high single-engine safety speed, particularly in the case of the Mk.II. My remit was to investigate this shortcoming and report on it.

The Beaufighter was essentially a night fighter, so the take-off problem was compounded by the aircraft's role. However, it was very effective in that role by virtue of having Airborne Interception radar and a powerful armament of 4×20 mm nose cannon and 6×0.303-in machine guns.

Entry to the aircraft was through a floor hatch and over the folded seatback into a roomy cockpit with a fine all-round view, in spite of the mighty engines protruding well ahead of the pilot on each side. Although the Merlins were quite wide apart along the 57 ft 10 in span, the three-bladed fully feathering Hydromatic airscrews looked as if they could have touched the fuselage if it had extended far

enough forward. It was obvious from this layout that there would be a powerful asymmetric moment in the event of an engine failure.

Before I started my investigation I made a general handling flight to get the feel of the aeroplane. Take-off proved to be unexpectedly demanding because, as the throttles were advanced and power increased, the terrific propwash gave marked gyroscopic effects as the tail was raised and the rudder seemed unable to hold the swing without the aid of considerable differential use of the throttles after going through the CRUISING gate. Lift-off came at about 100 mph, just after full throttles had been reached, but this left a considerable gap to the 180 mph safety speed at maximum take-off weight quoted in the preliminary Pilot's Notes, even though the Beaufighter had good acceleration.

The aircraft showed neutral stability on

the climb at 170 mph, and in the cruise it was sensitive in pitch and could not be trimmed to fly hands off, which was far from ideal for a night fighter. All of the controls were moderately light and effective, but the rudder heavied up if large angles were applied.

The all-up stall at 104 mph was preceded by elevator buffeting for some 12 mph before the right wing and nose dropped gently. All-down, the stall warning was less pronounced and the right wing dropped sharply at 80 mph. In all cases recovery from the stall was straightforward and easy.

For landing the circuit was made at 170 mph, and then the flaps were set to 20 degrees and the undercarriage lowered. Speed was then reduced to 150 mph and full flap lowered. It was very noticeable at this stage of the final approach at 130 mph that the aircraft tended to hunt longitudinally if the spectacle-type control wheel was not held rigid. The speed could be allowed to decay to 115 mph as the airfield boundary was approached. Touchdown occurred at 90 mph, but a three-pointer was difficult to achieve because of the stick hunting. On the landing runout the aircraft was directionally unstable and required both rudder and harsh braking to control it. From this flight it was clear that the Beaufighter was a powerful aeroplane with delicate stability and a sharp stall, so I decided to start the tests at 10,000 ft. The aircraft was at an all-up weight of 21,000 lb. Full throttle was used throughout and engine rpm set at 2,800 for both engines.

There was very little difference between the action of the two engines when cut. A very slight difference was the amount of opposite aileron needed to counteract bank. I found that it was easier to hold down the starboard engine with opposite aileron than the port engine.

At 170 mph the action of the aircraft when one engine was cut was to swing flatly around the vertical axis, starting fast and becoming even faster. After the aircraft had swung through some 15–20 degrees, the live engine banked very suddenly and quickly over the dead engine. The nose did not drop, but indeed tended to rise if anything, while the bank continued unabated until the aircraft had rolled on to its back and entered a steepening downward spiral. Recovery could only be effected by opening up the dead engine. During this test 3,500 ft of height was lost.

I repeated the test, taking immediate corrective action, and the aircraft could be controlled without loss of height. Once control had been regained and the aeroplane was flying straight and level I found that threequarters rudder was required and considerable force, but only about one quarter aileron was needed, and this could be held on quite lightly. If the speed was, at any time, allowed to drop below 150 mph, there was a loss of height.

The test was repeated at 160 mph and 150 mph, and the effects were much the same except that the aircraft started to bank after a swing of about 10 degrees, and the rate of bank accelerated as speed was lowered. However, at speeds of 140 mph, 130 mph and 120 mph control could not be regained as the live engine banked over the top of the dead engine, the rate of bank and the height loss again accelerating as speed was lowered.

A selection of the test speeds with flaps lowered 15 degrees showed the same characteristics as with flaps fully up. However, another factor had to be introduced to simulate reality. That was pilot reaction time, which would probably at best be of the order of 1½ sec, which would probably equate to a 10 mph speed loss.

My conclusion as a result of these tests, bearing in mind the height and daylight conditions under which they were made, was that a safety speed of 180 mph should be recommended for a take-off weight of 21,000 lb, with a 5 mph increase for every 1,000 lb increase in all-up weight.

The early models of Beaufighter had longitudinal and directional stability problems, but these were eventually improved by increasing the tailplane dihedral to 12 degrees and introducing a long dorsal fin extension along the top of the rear fuselage as far as the navigator's bubble.

The Beaufighter in its various versions became an operational Jack-of-all-trades and master of quite a few, but it never could throw off that lethal Achilles' heel of an abnormally high single-engine safety speed. As engine power was increased and all-up weight grew in the later models, so the safety speed rose until, in the TF.X, it was 200 mph at a maximum all-up weight of 25,400 lb, thus making every take-off a very critical phase of flight.

The Beaufighter X with dorsal fin.

Chapter 12
Bristol Buckingham

Not much has been written about the Buckingham, because the timing of its birth was conducive to condemning it to obscurity. It really originated as a design to Air Ministry Specification B.2/41, which called for a fast medium day or night bomber carrying the maximum defensive armament compatible with high speed. However, this Specification was subjected to so many changes that it was eventually replaced in March 1942 by a new one designated Buckingham I/P1.

The first prototype flew on 4th February 1943 and, like the other three prototypes, was powered by Bristol Centaurus IV engines with a high-altitude rating. The first production machine flew on 12th February 1944, and all production models were powered by Centaurus VII or XI engines rated for medium altitude. By the end of 1944 a total of 54 Buckingham B.1s had been delivered to the RAF, who really found that they had no further use for it in Europe, but felt it might be useful in the Far East theatre of war.

The temperamental Bristol Buckingham.

One of the early production aircraft, KV309, was sent to RAE Farnborough for a handling assessment, and I flew this machine twice on 13th June 1944. The Buckingham was a mid-wing aeroplane of very robust and somewhat squat appearance, with a span of 71 ft 10 in and a length of 40 ft 10 in. Its fuselage was of light alloy semi-monocoque structure in three sections, and it had all-metal stressed skin wings and tail unit. The wings carried fabric-covered Frise ailerons and split flaps in six sections, while the tail unit comprised twin fins and fabric-covered rudders and metal elevators.

Buckingham KV309 was fitted with two 2,520 hp Centaurus XI 18-cylinder two-row air-cooled sleeve-valve radial engines with two-speed superchargers, driving four-bladed constant-speed fully-feathering propellers. 1,055 Imperial gallons of fuel was carried internally.

Armament consisted of 4×0.303-in fixed machine guns in the nose, 4×0.303-in guns in a Bristol hydraulically-operated dorsal turret, and two similar guns hydraulically operated in the ventral gondola position. 4,000 lb of bombs could be carried in an internal bomb bay, giving the aircraft a maximum weight of 38,050 lb. A crew of four was carried.

Entry to the cockpit was either through the navigator's hatch and over the back of the pilot's collapsible seat, or through the roof of the pilot's cockpit. Neither route was easy when one was wearing a parachute. The cockpit itself was very roomy, and I found the instruments and controls placed too far away and therefore difficult to reach when strapped in. The fuel tank selectors were very stiff to operate. View was good both ahead and to the side on the ground.

All of the controls had high circuit friction, particularly the rudders, which were almost immoveable. This, together with the poor castoring characteristics of the tailwheel, made taxying quite a chore, with heavy bursts of engine power and heavy braking often being necessary.

On take-off the aircraft had a powerful swing to the right which required differential throttle to counteract, and it was advisable to get the tail up early in the take-off run to get rudder effectiveness. Unstick at a normal loaded weight of 37,000 lb occurred at 105 mph, and although acceleration was good it left a huge speed gap before the single-engine safety speed of 220 mph was reached.

On the climb the aircraft was slightly longitudinally unstable, and had a mediocre initial rate of climb of 1,700 ft/min. In cruising flight the stability was neutral in pitch but showed peculiar characteristics in roll and yaw, as in both axes it was neutrally stable to starboard and unstable to port.

The Buckingham's harmony of control was very poor. The ailerons were moderately heavy and sluggish, and were particularly ineffective at lower speeds; the elevator was just right for such an aircraft, both in weight and sensitivity; the rudders were extremely stiff, which was particularly bad as they were needed a great deal owing to the instability in yaw and roll and the difficulty of control on one engine at low speeds.

Because of the lack of harmonisation of the controls the aeroplane had to be flown every inch of the way. Extremely judicious use had to be made of the rudder in turns to prevent large magnitudes of skid developing, for if any slip or skid did develop it was very difficult to regain the balance. In bumpy weather the Buckingham was not pleasant to fly because it was almost impossible to trim, and because of the constant small corrections that had to be made by both aileron and rudder.

I carried out stalls at 8,000 ft. The all-up stall occurred at 112 mph with a small amount of buffeting giving warning of its onset. At the stall the port wing dropped quite slowly and recovery was straight-forward. The all-down stall was at 92 mph, with a straight nose drop and easy recovery.

Asymmetric flight was next checked, and showed no problem at high cruise speeds, but at 170 mph with the engines set at +4 lb boost and 2,400 rpm a violent swing developed when the port engine was cut, and control could not be regained with rudder. The next speed tried was 200 mph with +6 lb boost and 2,400 rpm, when the starboard engine was cut. Control could be regained using half rudder, which gave a heavy foot load until trimmed out. When the port engine was cut at 200 mph under the same engine conditions it was more marginal to regain control because of the tendency of the aircraft to roll to port.

For landing, a circuit speed of 170 mph was comfortable, but as the undercarriage was lowered the aircraft lurched from side to side and I was very aware of the sluggish aileron control. Once the flaps were lowered a speed of 140 mph was held until I was on the final approach at 120 mph, when the poor response of all of the controls was very evident, particularly as the hold-off at 110 mph was attempted, when the lag in the spring tab elevator response caused me to check too late on my first landing and then overcorrect on the second in trying to overcome the lag. In both cases the soft undercarriage eased the end result.

However, the worst was yet to come, for once the tail was on the ground the aircraft was completely unstable directionally and could not be held on rudder alone without harsh braking. This serious problem had already been identified by Bristol test pilots, and as a result enlarged fins and rudders were cleared in May 1944 to be fitted to the tenth and subsequent production aircraft. This modification cured the directional instability on the ground and helped the asymmetric flight characteristics.

With a top speed of 330 mph at 12,000 ft, well below specification, the Buckingham was a nippy performer for its day in its class. Its service ceiling was only 25,000 ft, but it had a range of 2,240 miles at 15,000 ft at 200 mph.

In the event the Buckingham never saw war service, and only 54 were built as bombers and 65 were converted to fast courier transports without armament and with extra fuel tankage for 3,000 miles. None of these aircraft amassed many flying hours, although the basic design survived in the form of the Buckmaster trainer for Brigand pilots.

The early production version of the Buckingham as I flew it was a poor aeroplane, and in spite of the tail unit modification still had inherent stability problems. In this respect it is interesting to note that one aircraft, KV322, was fitted with a central dorsal fin for stability tests. Certainly the Buckingham was a touchy aeroplane to fly in any form, and kept the pilot on his mettle – especially during take-off and landing and in stormy weather.

The Buckingham B1 in flight.

Chapter 13
Chance-Vought Cutlass

The advanced state of aviation technology in Germany at the end of the Second World War made a tremendous impact on the Allied victors, and no single aircraft impressed more than the Messerschmitt Me 163 rocket interceptor. It was not the operational record of the Komet, but the design concept that startled the world. Although the rocket motor was a sensational innovation, it was not in itself considered a practical power unit except for research aircraft, but the combination of sweptback wings and a tailless layout grabbed the imagination.

I made a considerable number of flights in the Me 163 and was very favourably impressed by its stability and control characteristics. Subsequently I was to fly some British tailless designs which failed to emulate these flight characteristics, notably the jet D.H.108 Swallow and the G.A.L./56 glider, both of which proved highly dangerous, mainly due to inherent longitudinal instability.

When I was appointed Resident British Test Pilot at the US Naval Air Test Center (NATC) at Patuxent River in 1951, tailless designs had already gained a reputation for

The Chance-Vought XF7U-1 Cutlass during catapult trials at Naval Air Test Center, Patuxent River.

The Chance-Vought Cutlass 3 on its carrier trials.

malevolence, so I was therefore most interested to seek out information on American experience in this field. Most of the emphasis on tailless design had come from the Northrop Aircraft Corporation, with its four-engined XB-35 bomber, XP-56 single-seat piston-engine fighter, and XP-79 single-seat jet fighter which crashed on its first flight. My interest, however, centred on the twin-jet Northrop X-4, because of its general similarity to the D.H.108. The NACA report made available to me showed that above M=0.68 the aircraft became longitudinally unstable at moderate lift coefficients, and that because of undamped small amplitude oscillations about all three axes at high Mach numbers, tests were not carried beyond M=0.93. Altogether, this was not a very encouraging view of British and American tailless designs.

When I was introduced to the stable of aircraft in Flight Test, to which I was assigned at Pax River, I was fascinated to find the tailless Chance-Vought XF7U-1 Cutlass included, and a quaint looking bird it was. It was a mid-wing, single-seat, naval interceptor fighter with wings of almost delta planform and twin vertical tails but no horizontal tail. Its unusual appearance was accentuated by its long, stalky, nosewheel.

The wings spanned 38 ft 8 in, were swept back 35 degrees and had an aspect ratio of 3, an incidence of 0 degrees, and a dihedral angle of 0 degrees. The vertical tails were swept back 45 degrees. Length was 41 ft 3 in, and the all-up weight 21,300 lb.

The aircraft was powered by two 3,200 lb static thrust Westinghouse J34-WE-34 engines, intended eventually to be fitted with afterburners. Fuel capacity was 971 US gallons. Armament was four 20 mm nose cannon.

From the pilot's viewpoint the most interesting feature of the Cutlass was its unconventional control system. Longitudinal and lateral control was by means of elevons (or ailavators, as the Chance-Vought firm preferred to call them) at the outer wing trailing edge. The ailavator installation incorporated an irreversible hydraulic boost system, so that when the pilot moved the stick he actuated an hydraulic valve, which moved the ailavators as dictated by the amount of stick displacement.

Since the longitudinal and lateral control boost system were irreversible, and therefore no aerodynamic force from the control surface was felt by the pilot, a simulated feel system was provided. Elevator stick force was simulated by a feel system which utilised ram air to impose loads on the control stick, varying as a function of surface displacement and dynamic air pressure as in an aircraft with a mechanical control system. Aileron feel was simulated by an aileron centering spring which provided the same force for a given lateral stick deflection regardless of airspeed. This was necessary because the artificial forces required for longitudinal feel were too large for desired lateral stick forces. Elevator and aileron trim actuators were provided to change the neutral position of the control stick as required for trimming either the elevator or aileron feel system.

Each ailavator had a combination balance trim tab and a spring tab. In boosted flight the spring tab was locked in the neutral position, and the balance trim tabs were inoperative. When manual reversion was engaged, the spring tab was automatically unlocked and the electrical circuits connecting the longitudinal and lateral trim switches to both feel system trim actuators were changed over automatically to operate the ailavator trim tabs instead.

The aircraft was also fitted with a pitch and yaw damper and hydraulically operated controllable full-span wing slats. Hydraulically operated, split-flap type variable position speed brakes formed the trailing edge of the wing centre-section, a relief valve in the system permitting them to open to an extent that was inversely proportional to airspeed. There were also two perforated under-fuselage speed brakes.

Another unusual feature of the Cutlass was its undercarriage, the main legs of which could be rotated 18 in aft from the take-off setting to permit an approximate 3 in decrease in landing attitude. Vanes on the periphery of the nosewheel caused wheel spin-up to occur before landing and thus reduced strut drag loads applied in landing. The brakes were power boosted, giving low pedal force and positive action.

I first flew the model XF7U-1 serial 124419 on 21st October 1951. In spite of its exaggerated nose-up ground attitude, it was quite easy to taxy because of the powerful brakes, but it had a tendency to weathercock in even moderate side winds. Rudder control effectiveness in a cross-wind take-off was unsatisfactory until a speed of 60 knots was reached. Up to that point directional control was dependent on the use of brakes. Unstick occurred at 105 knots if the aircraft was left to fly itself off, and it was unwise to try and pull it off earlier because of the proximity of the tail booms to the ground. The climb was laborious, and there was a distinct immediate impression that the aircraft was underpowered.

In flight the longitudinal stability was unsatisfactory at high indicated airspeeds and at high altitude, and the longitudinal control was too sensitive near the neutral position, which would make formation flying particularly difficult.

The irreversible power control system applied to the ailavators was, in my opinion, mechanically unsound, and manual reversion gave large out-of-trim forces because all trimming of the controls in their powered state was done on the feel system and not on the hinge moment which asserted itself when power was lost. The rate of longitudinal feel trim at slow speeds was also not fast enough for comfort.

Lateral control force stability was noticeably synthetic, and the 'springyness' associated with the stick centering was objectionable. The strong stick centering was poorly damped, and this, coupled with the sensitivity of the lateral control near the neutral position, caused overcontrolling and made precision flying difficult.

Lateral trim characteristics were unsatisfactory. It was difficult to make small adjustments in lateral trim because of the sensitivity of the lateral control system.

The rate of roll was excellent, being 250 degrees per second at 250 knots, but an undesirable amount of adverse yaw was encountered in rolling manoeuvres. Although this high rate of roll was impressive, it was unnecessarily excessive because it could not really be utilised in combat.

Dynamic lateral-directional characteristics were bad without the yaw damper functioning, but the latter was most effective in controlling the aircraft's Dutch rolling tendencies in turbulent air.

The maximum Mach number I attained in a steep dive was M=0.96. There was a sharp nose-down pitch at M=0.90, but this condition disappeared with continued acceleration, although in recovery there were signs that elevator effectiveness was beginning to fall off. The high altitude buffet boundary was very low, being about 2.1 g at M=0.82 at 40,000 ft, which seriously limited the aircraft's tactical usefulness as a fighter. The speed brakes were very effective in reducing the speed of the aircraft and they produced no buffet, but their extension resulted in a nose-down pitching moment which was undesirable for high Mach number dive recovery.

There was insufficient ailavator to stall the aircraft except dynamically, when a wing drop usually resulted. Handling characteristics with asymmetric engine power were very satisfactory in normal flight, and were reasonable for airfield landing.

I was particularly interested in the catapulting and deck-landing characteristics of the Cutlass. The catapulting trials at Pax River revealed the large amount of longitudinal rotation required to develop maximum lift at the end of the catapult power stroke. Deck landing also presented a problem because of the very poor view caused by the approach at a speed of 110 knots, which put the aircraft at 20 degrees incidence.

Although it was unlikely that the XF7U-1 would ever see a carrier deck, it had an interesting arrester hook arrangement. A folding jointed hook was installed in the upper tailcone of the fuselage. When extended it was at an angle of 55 degrees below the centreline of the aircraft, and was capable of lateral deflections of 20 degrees to either side of the centreline. For carrier stowage the outer wings could be folded upwards, giving the aircraft a folded span of 21 ft 3¼ in, and a folded height of 15 ft.

The performance figures obtained at Pax River showed a maximum speed of 496 knots TAS at 20,000 ft; time to climb=16.3 min to 30,000 ft; service ceiling=38,000 ft; range=975 nm at 400 knots TAS at 30,000 ft.

The XF7U-1 Cutlass was, in effect, a total failure. It was underpowered, overcomplicated, and a non-starter for carrier operations. I regard it as a test bed for the irreversible powered control system with completely artificial feel, and in this case not a very successful application. The system found favour with designers because it permitted manoeuvres at high sonic, transonic, and supersonic speeds, and also it masked stick fixed instability, particularly in the transonic range. This second reason is a dangerous one, since failure of either the power system or the artificial feel system may lead to the abrupt application of large control surface deflections at high speeds, with attendant high aerodynamic forces and moments – a recipe for disaster.

In spite of the severe shortcomings of the first model of the Cutlass, the US Navy allowed Chance-Vought to continue development, but it was obvious that the improvements required would considerably alter the external shape and internal-engineering of the successor model.

The development of the XF7U-1 Cutlass from a reject to an acceptable fighter would obviously involve some radical redesign, particularly in the power-operated controls. Chance-Vought had formulated its views in this area as a result of their experiences in the flight trials of the prototype, and these were stated as follows:

a The best application for delta-type aircraft is a power-operated irreversible system with artificial feel for the ailavators or elevons, and a low boost ratio reversible system for the rudder.

b Artificial feel is required for the satisfactory operation of tactical aircraft. Feel for other than simple trimmable centering springs is required for elevator and rudder, e.g. for the elevator, a system which is a function of dynamic pressure and surface displacement. Simple trimmable self-centering springs provide adequate feel for ailerons.

c Tests of the power strut and servo valve in a mockup may be misleading; it is necessary to install and test these units in the actual aircraft components in which they are to be installed.

d It is desirable to make the power control system and the utility systems independent of each other.

e Only limited control requirements can be met by manual reversion after a power system failure unless an impossibly complex design is sought after. It would seem that a duplication of the power-operated system with no manual standby is preferable to a power-operated system plus a limited standby.

So much for the theory, but the proof of its soundness would be revealed in the flight testing. Certainly the XF7U-1 had some unpleasant characteristics when the control system malfunctioned, which it was prone to do, and any high aero-dynamic forces thus induced were especially dangerous in the light of the low structural limits to which US fighter aircraft were built at that time (a limit load factor of 7.3 g with a design ultimate factor of 1.5). The maintenance aspects of the complex powered-control system were also considered unsuitable for front-line squadron service.

The F7U-3 arrived at Pax River in the summer of 1952, and my first impression was that it had grown somewhat in physical stature from its predecessor. The span had increased to 39 ft 8½ in and the length to 43 ft 9½ in. The all-up weight was 28,300 lb, with an overload maximum of 33,200 lb.

The engines were two 3,960 lb static thrust Westinghouse J46-WE-8 axial flow turbojets fitted with afterburners to increase the thrust of each engine to 5,800 lb. Fuel capacity had been increased to 1,320 US gallons, and armament was four 20 mm side-fuselage cannon. External stores could be carried (thirty-two 2.75 in rockets plus two 2,000 lb bombs).

The main external changes made in the F7U-3, as compared with the XF7U-1, were:

a Larger dorsal fins, and auxiliary rudder area increased by 4 ft^2 to improve directional stability at low speeds.

b Ailavator chord increased by 12 in and trailing edges blunted.

c Fuselage increased in depth and width by 12 in to house the extra fuselage tanks and electronic equipment.

d Static ground angle increased from 9 to 13 degrees, thus eliminating the need for the originally projected F7U-3 design of a nosewheel oleo strut which extended as the aircraft was tensioned on the catapult.

e Redesigned nose and cockpit canopy to give improved view for deck landing.

f Arrester hook changed from sting type to V-frame type and relocated farther forward on underside of the fuselage.

However, the most fundamental change was an internal one to the control system. In place of manual reversion there was incorporated a dual boost system with two separate and distinct systems, each driven by two hydraulic pumps, one on each engine, so that in the event of engine failure both systems continued to operate at reduced rates of flow but at full power. The two systems fed tandem boost cylinders capable of providing 30,000 ft/lb hinge moment at the ailavator. With the engines dead but windmilling, sufficient power was generated to drive the power control system under all conditions of flight, except that at flare to land the airspeed was marginal for full pump output. To ensure sufficient power below 175 knots airspeed and 2,000 ft altitude, a separate hydraulic pump driven from a battery (used only for that purpose) and pilot-selected was provided. The battery gave a pump operation endurance of 2½ min.

The directional stability when taxying was unsatisfactory, probably due to a combination of excessive lift from the increased static ground attitude and extremely sensitive brakes. My first take-off was made on 19th August 1952 in F7U-3 serial 128454, and I found engine acceleration to be very poor. Opening up from idle rpm to full power took 23 sec, so the aircraft had to be held on the brakes until at least 95% power was reached, otherwise a long take-off run resulted. As with its predecessor, the F7U-3 had to be steered on the brakes until a speed of 60 knots was reached, when rudder control became effective.

Because of its high ground attitude the aircraft virtually flew itself off at 100 knots. The climb was leisurely, and again there was the feeling of being underpowered. At this stage in development afterburners were not permitted to be used for take-off because of their temperamental behaviour, but on the ascent they could more than treble the rate of climb.

In flight the static longitudinal control was weakly positive to neutral, and the stick force per 'g' was rather high (about 10 lb) at high speeds. The lateral control was too sensitive through the neutral stick position, and tended to make the pilot over-control. Rate of roll was excellent, but the control force for full deflection exceeded the desired maximum value of 20 lb. Directional stability was satisfactory at high indicated airspeeds, but deteriorated at lower speeds.

As regards stability and control, in addition to the faults already listed there were two particularly tedious short-comings. First was the necessity for continuous retrimming in all three planes with any speed change. Second, with the yaw and pitch dampers inoperative the flight characteristics were completely unsuitable tactically, as any attempt by the pilot to damp induced oscillations in any plane merely aggravated the situation.

The high Mach number characteristics were a mild nose-down trim change at M=0.89 to 0.95 with a tendency to oscillate in pitch. Ailavator effectiveness deteriorated above M=0.95, but was satisfactory for dive recovery at M=1.02. The speed brakes were very good, being fast operating and giving excellent deceleration, negligible trim change and only moderate buffet beyond three-quarters extension. However, a serious tactical deficiency of the aircraft was its low buffet boundary at high altitude.

The stall or, rather, minimum speed characteristics, were very good in the landing configuration, but were un-satisfactory with the slats retracted. In the latter case a sudden and excessive yaw occurred at about 4 knots before the stall and was barely controllable.

Handling characteristics with asymmetric power had deteriorated in this model owing to the poor directional stability at low speeds and the lower power/weight ratio. Single-engine deck landing would have been an extremely hazardous undertaking, since lift control could too easily be lost on the approach in such circumstances.

Deck landing trials conducted on the USS *Midway* in the middle of August 1952 were a qualified success. Before the trials a new fuel control was fitted, and gasoline was used instead of JP-3 fuel, improving the engine acceleration characteristics to 15 sec from idle to 100% rpm, and 3 sec from 83% to 95% rpm. However, this fuel control was unsatisfactory for use at high altitude, and the use of gasoline necessitated a higher idling rpm setting to avoid excessive tailpipe temperatures during acceleration through the low rpm range. In this case the idle setting of 45% rpm gave a large amount of residual thrust which required heavy braking to counteract it during airfield landings.

The deck-landing approach speed was 110 knots at 24,000 lb AUW. Speed and height control could best be regulated by use of speed brakes and elevator control whilst leaving the engines at a fixed setting of 82% to 84% rpm. The approach speed was critical for controlling rate of descent, and a reduction of 5 knots could result in an uncontrollable sink. On receiving the 'cut' signal a slight forward pressure on the stick was required, but no flare needed to be made. The view at the approach incidence of 21 degrees was barely acceptable. Folded span was 22 ft 3¾ in, and folded height was 14 ft 4 in.

When the aircraft was flown at the high nose-up attitudes required for low-speed flight, a substantial amount of fuel was trapped in the forward centre-section tanks. At 18.4 degrees attitude this amounted to 65 US gallons, and at 28 degrees attitude it increased to 130 US gallons.

Catapult take-offs were made down to 29 knots windspeed over the deck at an AUW of 28,300 lb, but that was the minimum windspeed for safety. Full aft stick was required at the end of the catapult power stroke to fly away cleanly. After these shipboard trials, a further series of catapult tests was made on the airfield at the Naval Air Test Center, with launches up to the maximum AUW of 33,200 lb.

The performance figures obtained at Pax River showed a maximum speed of 552 knots TAS at 5,000 ft, and 607 knots TAS at sea level with afterburners. Time to climb was 10 min to 30,000 ft, or 3 min with afterburners; the service ceiling was 45,000 ft, and the range 1,165 nm at 500 knots TAS at 38,700 ft.

The F7U-3 was a considerable improvement over the earlier model Cutlass, although it had deteriorated in some respects, mainly with regard to directional stability. The fact that there was no manual reversion in the power control system was probably in its favour, for the hydraulic system had been made as foolproof as one could imagine, and the XF7U-1 control problems were largely attributable to the incorporation of a highly inefficient manual reversion system.

The Cutlass, in whatever version, was not a pleasant aircraft to fly, and I often wonder why the US Navy persevered with its development after experience on the XF7U-1. Perhaps it was because in the growth area of the swept wing the delta planform offered an exciting advance that could not be ignored, and the US Navy wanted experience in operating such new designs to test their compatibility with carrier operations. In my book, it looked ugly, flew badly, and was a menace anywhere near a carrier deck. Somebody should have terminated development after the first model, but having passed up that option, Chance-Vought made a brave attempt to make the best of a bad job.

Chapter 14
Cierva C.30A Rota

The Autogiro was the brainchild of Juan de la Cierva, a Spanish civil engineer. In 1919 a trimotor aeroplane he had designed crashed after stalling at low altitude, and this fired his determination to develop an aircraft that could not stall, and to this he gave the trade name Autogiro.

Cierva's genius lay in his development of the flapping rotor, thus providing the link between the fixed-wing aeroplane and the rotary-wing helicopter. His prototype C.30 two-seat Autogiro featured a freely-tilting 37 ft diameter rotor directly linked to a hanging stick for the pilot. The rotor hub was mounted on top of a four-strut pylon just forward of the pilot's cockpit. The three cantilever rotor blades were built on tubular steel spars with spruce ribs, plywood-skinned with fabric covering. There were no control surfaces, but only a differential stabiliser to counter engine torque. It was powered by a 105 hp Armstrong Siddeley Genet Major I. The autogiro delivered to RAE was a production C.30A Rota, K4775, powered by a 140 hp Armstrong Siddeley Civet I, the RAF designation for the Genet Major IA, driving a two-bladed metal propeller.

The RAE conducted extensive tests over a period of almost two years, and the handling aspects as described by Flt Lt H.P. Fraser make interesting reading.

The take-off was accomplished in three stages, the first of which involved starting the rotor with the aircraft stationary. One precaution necessary in wind speeds above 25 mph was to head the Autogiro at right angles to the wind with its right side facing into wind, to ensure that the advancing blade, i.e. the blade moving forward on the left of the pilot, did not advance into wind when rotor rpm were low, as the small centrifugal force would not keep the flapping amplitude within safe limits.

With the wheel brakes on and the pilot's right hand holding the control column in its locked position, the throttle was opened to 1,000 rpm. The left hand then released the rotor brake lever, pushing it to the bottom of its quadrant, moving it inwards so that it took up its function as the clutch lever, and then easing it up the inner quadrant until the blades started to rotate. The control column was then released from its locked position by the right hand and eased back slightly, while the left hand operated a single lever to release the wheel brakes and disengage the clutch simultaneously.

The Autogiro would now start to move forwards, and when facing into wind the throttle had to be opened immediately, as the rotor would have begun to decelerate because of insufficient airflow through the rotor disc to maintain autorotation. To obtain the best acceleration the stick was held forward to hold the rotor disc at minimum incidence and keep rotor drag as low as possible. During that procedure the pilot had to keep his feet firmly on the rudder bar, with a slight push to the right to hold the aircraft straight. Actually there was no rudder, and the bar was in fact a tailwheel steering device.

Sufficient airspeed to establish autorotation was normally obtained in about 3 sec, then the stick was eased slowly but firmly back to its full extent to lift the Autogiro off the ground. The length of the ground run and the time taken to lift off depended on the wind strength, the rotor revolutions, and the load. The take-off run as measured in still air at the RAE was 450 ft at full load of 1,900 lb.

The Cierva C.30A Rota Autogiro on take-off.

Once the Autogiro was airborne the stick had to be eased forward to obtain the best climbing speed; thus it took a distance of 1,510 ft to reach a height of 50 ft. The maximum rate of climb was 355 ft/min, and the service ceiling a mere 6,600 ft.

In normal cruising flight the Rota was very simple to handle, but with some lag in the fore and aft control and rather heavy lateral control, especially in steep turns, which were possible up to 45 degrees. If the bank was increased beyond that value the nose dropped and a spiral commenced, with the risk of exceeding the safe limit of speed. Although both the longitudinal and lateral bias controls were effective trimmers, the Autogiro was inherently unstable, especially in bumpy weather.

To increase speed the nose had to be pushed down until, at 115 mph, the Rota became nose-heavy, and as the speed increased so did the nose-heaviness.

Probing of this area showed evidence that loss of control would probably occur if the maximum permissible speed of 140 mph was exceeded. The maximum attainable speed in level flight was 94 mph.

Slow-speed flight was of course one of the assets of the Autogiro, but slow flying close to the ground, besides being a matter of practice, required an understanding of the limitations imposed by four facts:

1 For a given throttle setting the ratio of the increase in the rate of climb for an increase in speed above the minimum level speed was low, and less than the ratio of the increase in the rate of descent for the same decrease in the speed below minimum level speed.

2 There was a large time lag in the fore and aft control.

3 The control column could not be pushed forward too quickly to increase speed, or the Rota would sink bodily on to the ground before it had had time to change its attitude slightly nose down and increase speed.

4 The lag in the lateral control was small, but a fairly large angle of bank had to be reached before the Rota began to turn.

The cumulative effect of these characteristics was that the fore and aft control could not bring about the necessary adjustments in attitude and speed in level flight quickly enough to compensate for bumps without adjustments in throttle setting. Similarly, turns could not be made without sideslip, so engine power had to be increased to prevent loss of height at slow speed. The minimum level speed was 32 mph at 1,900 lb, and 23½ mph at 1,560 lb.

Steep descents, with or without engine power, were straightforward, but changes in throttle setting or alterations in pitch produced a slight yaw. If the forward speed was allowed to get too low, the lateral control ceased to be effective and the Rota swung quickly to the right through about 180 degrees and dropped its nose. This vortex ring state was the equivalent of the stall in a fixed-wing aircraft, and recovery was similar. The steepest angle of controlled glide was 45 degrees, and the lowest gliding speed was 22 mph with a rate of descent of 30 ft/sec. The view downwards was obstructed at all times by the shape of the fuselage, and ahead when the nose was high, as in slow flying.

The landing was made with the engine throttled right back, with a minimum gliding speed of 40 mph just before flattening out gradually from about 10 ft above the ground to about 2 ft, when the braking action of the rotor disc slowed the Autogiro and the control column could be pulled back to effect a three-pointer.

Although there was no need for the pilot to keep his feet on the rudder bar during normal flight, it was essential to have them on when landing to control the steerable tailwheel during the short ground run. It was essential to ensure that there was no drift on touchdown, and also to push the control column forward to keep the aircraft firmly on the ground by spilling air out of the rotor.

Although it was not simple to fly to its limits, the Cierva C.30 was the most successful Autogiro ever built, about 180 being produced in Britain, France and Germany. Demonstrating his confidence in his own design, Cierva himself made the first flight in the C.30 in April 1933. However, the RAE criticised the lack of separate rudder and elevator surfaces, and was of the opinion that the latter were essential for safety in a high-speed dive. Nevertheless, the C.30 operated effectively in many parts of the world.

Chapter 15
Consolidated Liberator

The first time I learned of the Consolidated B-24 Liberator was during aircraft recognition classes in the Fleet Air Arm, and the first time I saw one was in the winter of 1941 while on fighter patrol in a Grumman Wildcat (then named Martlet) from the escort carrier HMS *Audacity*, covering a convoy in the Bay of Biscay. This airborne whale was not in much danger of being attacked, as it was easily recognisable with its bulky fuselage, high-aspect-ratio Davis wing, and almost circular twin fins and rudders. The four-engined, high-wing reconnaissance bomber had just entered service with RAF Coastal Command, and its very long range and its useful weapons-carrying capability made it a most welcome entrant into the Atlantic theatre.

Time moved on, and by good fortune I found myself given the opportunity to fly a Liberator V at RAE Farnborough on 3rd June 1944. I had been doing a series of tests on the Halifax and Lancaster to determine their behaviour after failure of an outer engine, and the Liberator was to be similarly tested for comparison. At the

The grand old warrior – the Consolidated Liberator.

same time I was to report on its general handling characteristics.

This particular B-24D Liberator V, BZ767/G, was, as can be seen by the /G designation, still on the Secret List because of some of the equipment aboard. It was powered by four 1,200 hp Pratt & Whitney Twin Wasp R-1830-43 14-cylinder two-row radial engines driving three-bladed Hamilton Hydromatic propellers. The armament consisted of two electrically driven turrets, each with 2×0.5 in guns, one in the tail and one in a dorsal position just behind the cockpit, and six manual 0.5 in guns (one in the nose, two in the sides of the nose, two in beam positions and one in the ventral tunnel). The maximum bomb load was 12,800 lb.

This version of the Liberator introduced outer-wing fuel cells, so it had a take-off weight of 52,000 lb when I flew it. The view from the cockpit was surprisingly restricted on the ground, but taxying was made very easy by the tricycle under-carriage. For take-off, half flap was lowered and the engine cowl gills were closed. Even applying almost full power before releasing the brakes, the acceleration was poor and the take-off run long to unstick at 115 mph. As soon as the safety speed of 150 mph was reached the cowl gills were opened fully, the fuel and hydraulic booster pumps switched off, and speed set to 145 mph for the climb. If the climb was continued above 10,000 ft the fuel booster pumps had to be switched on again.

Stability on the climb and in cruising flight was positive about all three axes, and the controls, which were all fabric covered, were effective but very heavy. It really was like driving a London bus rather than flying an aeroplane. Thank heaven it had a wonderful autopilot. Although I had only a flight engineer with me, the Liberator V normally carried a crew of ten including two pilots, but I thought the pilot's view for attacking or countering an attack was poor, rather like that of a modern airliner pilot.

The Twin Wasp engines of the Liberator had single-stage engine-driven super-chargers and exhaust-driven turbo-super-chargers, and control of the engines was unusual. On run-up after warm-up the throttles were opened up to their stops, and then the blowers were opened up until the boost reached 47 in with the blower levers on their adjustable stops. On take-off the throttles were opened fully and thereafter left there for all phases of flight, and boost was regulated by the blower levers except when flying at boosts obtainable without the turbos, when the required boost minus 1 or 2 in had to be set by the throttles and the extra 1 or 2 in set by the blower levers to keep the blowers turning. It was all very complicated, hence the necessity to carry a flight engineer.

The tests on engine failure characteristics showed that if an outer engine was cut the aircraft yawed vigorously and swung over into a dive which reached about 45 degrees, so that the limiting speed of 310 mph indicated airspeed was reached fairly quickly. Corrective action had to be taken by throttling back the opposite outer engine and easing out of the dive. The time from cut to correcting movement of the controls was 17 sec, which compared favourably with 10 sec on the Halifax and 15 sec on the Lancaster.

In normal circumstances of an engine failure the Liberator could be trimmed to fly hands-off at a comfortable 150 mph, and in the event of two engines failing on one side the speed was not to be allowed to fall below 140 mph, in order to have sufficient rudder trim to hold the asymmetric moment, and 10 degrees of flap was advisable for manoeuvring.

For normal landing the hydraulic booster pump and fuel booster pumps were switched on and the cowl gills shut. The undercarriage was lowered at 170 mph, and the blowers left as set for cruising at reduced powers. The flaps were lowered threequarters-down at 155 mph and an engine assisted approach made at 120 mph. The rate of descent was high in this configuration, and had to be checked

The B-24D Liberator V.

before touchdown. The landing run was long and considerable braking was required.

Although the Liberator appeared on the scene some four years after the Flying Fortress, it had only a very small advantage in speed or range over the B-17 and was more complicated to fly and handled less well. However, it had more development potential, and 19,203 were built, more than any other single type of American aircraft. It unquestionably proved a boon to Coastal Command and, although I have never heard any pilot wax lyrical about its flying qualities, it proved to be a good solid performer, or, as an ex-Liberator pilot put it, a grand old warrior. That makes a fitting epitaph for the B-24.

Chapter 16
Dewoitine D.520

At the outbreak of the Second World War the French Air Force had three single-seat fighters in service – the Morane-Saulnier MS.406, the Curtiss H.75 and the Bloch MB.152. The contemporary German fighter, the Bf 109E, had two big advantages over all three in the matter of speed and rate of climb.

The arrival into service in 1940 of the Dewoitine D.520 low-wing single-seat fighter gave the French pilots a reasonable chance of survival against the Messerschmitt Bf 109E, as was clearly shown when Germany's top ace in the Spanish Civil War Condor Legion, Werner Moelders, was shot down by a D.520 over France and taken prisoner for a very brief spell.

The D.520 was certainly a good-looking aeroplane. With the cockpit set aft of the trailing edge of the wings, it looked like a long-nosed Spitfire, but there the similarity ended, for the D.520 was not in the same class as a fighting aeroplane, and was quite a handful to fly.

It was powered by a 910 hp Hispano-

The tricky Dewoitine D.520.

Suiza 12Y liquid-cooled engine driving a three-bladed Ratier propeller with automatic rpm control for a given power setting, a sluggish system that led to overspeeding in dives. The engine was also very prone to cut-out under the influence of negative 'g', which was a decided disadvantage against the Bf 109 with its fuel injection engine which allowed it to bunt into a steep dive as a combat escape manoeuvre. In fact the D.520 could outdive the German fighter, but could not use this asset tactically because of the limitations of its engine and propeller. The French machine had a limiting dive speed of 415 mph, but this was often exceeded by its impetuous Gallic pilots.

Right from the moment I entered the cockpit I sensed that this was an aeroplane that would have to be flown every inch of the way. The view from the cockpit was terrible, and made taxying difficult, especially as I had to make a determined mental effort to familiarise myself with the French system of throttle movement on pre-Second World War aircraft, which was the reverse to that used by the British.

Take-off required strong left rudder to counteract the directional swing, but once airborne with the undercarriage retracted, the aircraft's initial rate of climb at 135 mph was impressive at about 4,000 ft/min. The rate of climb gradually began to fall off, and was slightly less than that of the Bf 109E up to 12,000 ft and about the same up to 20,000 ft, but thereafter the 520 became the better because of its more efficient supercharger at that height.

In level flight the D.520 was marginally stable about all axes, but was sensitive directionally to changes of power and snaked badly in turbulence, making it difficult to aim accurately. Its armament consisted of 4×7.5 mm wing machine-guns with 675 rounds per gun, and a 1×20 mm Hispano-Suiza cannon with 60 rounds, firing through the airscrew spinner.

The aircraft had good acceleration in the dive, but the moveable tailplane had a tendency to lock at high speed, so it was advisable to set it at the desired setting to assist pull-out before entering the dive.

The Achilles' heel of the D.520 as a fighter was its stall under 'g'. The level flight stall with flaps and undercarriage retracted occurred at 90 mph without any warning and with a severe wing drop. The same characteristics were evidenced in the 'g' stall, and unless recovery action was immediate a spin, or at worst an inverted spin, was likely to develop. Although the flight manual advised that voluntary spinning was prohibited, I let myself get into a spin while exploring the manoeuvre limits of the D.250, for it was a very manoeuvrable aeroplane and I felt that its reputation for bad spin behaviour was probably exaggerated. How wrong I was! The spin rotation was rapid, and I immediately applied corrective action only to find that I had merely reversed the direction of the spin, so I let the rotation and attitude stabilise before again taking corrective action. This was effective, but not until another two full turns had been completed, and then a steep dive ensued with considerable height loss. My height loss from entry to full recovery was almost 10,000 ft. It is easy to understand, therefore, the reluctance of squadron pilots to take the D.520 to the limits of its manoeuvre envelope.

The maximum level flight speed of the D.520 was only 329 mph, while that of the Bf 109E was some 25 mph faster at medium altitude, although the differential narrowed below 15,000 ft. This discrepancy in performance between two adversaries that were otherwise fairly well matched except in the matter of fire-power, where again the Messerschmitt was superior, meant that the German fighter always had the edge.

The Dewoitine was a real maverick when it came to landing, although it was really only in the last 100 yards of the landing run that the problems occurred. The approach with wheels and flaps lowered was made with power at 95 mph to give a touchdown at 80 mph. Then, as the tail lowered on to the runway, one was immediately aware of the deterioration in directional control as the speed dissipated. This was mainly due to the blanking of the rudder by the fuselage in the tail-down attitude, and any tendency to swing was aggravated by the turning moment of the wide-track undercarriage.

I had been warned of these wayward characteristics, and told to counteract them by short stabs on the slow-acting pneumatic brakes, accompanied by judicious bursts of engine power. That worked but it felt knife-edge, as indeed the D.520's accident/incident rate on landing clearly testified, with one such accident every 200 flight hours. The frequent ground loops could be serious, causing nose-overs and collapsed undercarriages. The inward collapse of an undercarriage leg did not normally cause bad damage, as this was in the direction of retraction, but an outward collapse usually badly damaged the wing and required extensive repairs. Even moderately fast taxying risked the possibility of a ground loop, and one French pilot remarked, 'That little she-devil is never to be trusted till she is in the hangar'.

The D.520 was used by the Vichy French in North Africa, where it was in action against Allied carrier aircraft during Operation Torch in late 1942. Seven D.520s were shot down by Sea Hurricanes and Seafires without loss to the British fighters, and that just about puts the Dewoitine fighter in perspective with its contemporaries.

The D.520 was one of those very rare examples of an aeroplane that 'looked good but did not fly good'. It was not all bad, but what was bad was very bad. Certainly it was not up with the state of the art of its contemporary allies and enemies.

Chapter 17
Dornier Do 18

The Dornier Do 18 flying-boat was originally produced as a trans-atlantic mail-carrier, and was used on the South Atlantic service of Deutsche Lufthansa in the second half of the 1930s. The prototype first flew on 15th March 1933 and was powered by two 540 hp Junkers Jumo 5 diesel engines. The next four boats, designated Do 18Es, were fitted with 600 hp Jumo 205C diesels, and a sixth designated Do 18F was heavier and had a greater wing area than the previous versions. This latter aircraft set an international straight line nonstop distance

record for seaplanes of 5,214 miles, from Start Point, England, to Caravellas, Brazil, on 27–29 March 1938. It was later fitted with a pair of 880 hp BMW 132N radial engines and redesignated the Do 18L, and first flew in this form on 21st November 1939.

With war imminent, the Germans decided to use a military variant, the Do 18D, for reconnaissance, and the first such type was in operational service by September 1938. It was in effect an armed Do 18E, and one of these had the dubious honour of being the first Luftwaffe aircraft

The docile Dornier 18.

to fall to British guns, those of a Skua from the aircraft carrier *Ark Royal* on 26th September 1939.

The Do 18G supplanted the 18D in production early in 1939, and by September of that year, when production ceased, just over 100 Do 18s had been built, 70 being of the G type. It was one of the latter that I found at Schleswigsee marine base at the end of the war, and although it was not serviceable I got some German mechanics working on it. By September 1945 it was ready to fly. By that time I had flown four other types of German flying-boats and was getting my sea legs, so on 19 and 20 September I spent some time familiarising myself with the Do 18 on the waters of Schleswig Schlei.

The Dornier craft had sleek, pleasing lines with its slender, tapering hull, streamlined powerplant nacelle, and lack of wing floats. It had a high wing of low aspect ratio mounted on a pylon and braced to lateral sponsors which projected from the hull sides. The wing structure was of metal, covered with fabric except in the slipstream of the airscrew. The hull was an all-metal structure with the tailplane braced to it by parallel struts. The wing span was 77 ft 9 in, the length 63 ft 2 in, and the height 17 ft 9 in.

Power was provided by two 880 hp Junkers Jumo 205D 6-cylinder, double-opposed, water-cooled diesel engines mounted in tandem on the wing centre section pylon. The front engine drove a three-bladed metal airscrew direct, and the rear engine drove a similar airscrew through shafting. The radiators for both engines were in the leading edge of the pylon. Four fuel tanks amidships in the hull carried a total of 862.4 Imperial gallons.

Normally a crew of four was carried – pilot, navigator, wireless operator and gunner. Armament consisted of a single 13 mm MG 131 machine-gun in the bow position, and a single 20 mm MG 151 cannon in a power-operated hull turret. The empty weight of the boat was 12,900 lb and the loaded weight of 22,050 lb.

The control system was very simple. The elevators and rudder were aero-dynamically balanced, and auxiliary surfaces hinged slightly below the wing trailing edge acted as ailerons and landing flaps. A water rudder was situated at the extremity of the tapering step on the underside of the hull.

The cockpit was entered via a sliding canopy and was quite roomy with good view, although the instrument layout was rather haphazard. Starting up the Jumo diesels was quite a slow process, entailing pre-heating the torch plugs and raising pressure in the fuel lines by pilot handpump to 0.5 atu. The starting fuel tank had then to be pumped up to 3.5 atu, thus automatically priming the engine when it was turned over by the electric inertia starter. Once the engine fired the rpm stabilised at 600, which was a fast tick-over. The rear engine was normally started first, followed by the front, to keep noise and water spray to a minimum for the bowman who was eventually to release the mooring rope from the mooring buoy.

The Do 18 taxied comfortably and was easy to control directionally with use of the water rudder. Take-off with the flaps drooped one-third got the boat on to the step after a run with the wheel held just aft of neutral. Once on the step, acceleration was only moderate and the resultant overall run to unstick was lengthy. Surprisingly little spray was thrown on to the pilot's windscreen throughout this process. There is a danger with a long take-off run that porpoising can occur, but in my short experience with this flying-boat no such tendency was apparent.

Once airborne the Do 18 climbed at just over 1,000 ft/min and exhibited very positive stability around all three axes, with effective although rather heavy controls. In normal cruising flight at 180 mph the aircraft was rock steady, and fitted as it was with an effective autopilot would have been an excellent vehicle for long-range flying. The versions used by

Deutsche Lufthansa carried two pilots, a radio-operator and an engineer for its transatlantic flights, but the military Do 18G-1 had a reduced range of 2,174 miles, which was still outstanding.

The other splendid feature of the Do 18 was its single-engine characteristics. If an engine failed there were no asymmetric problems, and indeed, for maximum endurance flying, either engine could be stopped if required and later restarted in flight.

Perhaps the nicest aspect of this aircraft was its alighting qualities. On the approach at 65 mph with full flaps it was rock steady, and the attitude was such that only small backward movement of the control wheel was needed to flatten out over the water before touching down at 56 mph for a very short run-out.

The Do 18 was undoubtedly a very successful design with virtually no flying vices, an innovative engine layout, and a superb range. In its military adaptation it was obviously poorly defended against fighter attack, but as it normally operated well outside the range of land-based fighters it was a very useful reconnaissance vehicle for the Luftwaffe.

Of the two Second World War German flying-boat manufacturers, I always found that the Dornier products were easier to fly and instilled much more confidence than those of Blohm and Voss. The best boat I ever flew was the three-engined Do 24, but the Do 18 came a good second.

A Do 18D entering the water from its slipway.

Chapter 18
Dornier Do 24

As someone who had only very limited experience on flying-boats during my wartime Service career, I found myself plunged into an Aladdin's cave of these machines at the conclusion of the Second World War in Europe, when I moved into Schleswig-Holstein with the RAE team seeking out surviving German aircraft.

The marine bases at Kiel-Holtenau and Schleswigsee had a surprising number and variety of intact flying-boats, especially at the latter establishment. Both bases had small land airfields combined with large slipways and facilities for marine operations.

Schleswigsee lay on the inland sound called Schleswig Schlei, which was a long, narrow inlet running southwest from the Baltic Sea to finish up in two open basins at the town of Schleswig, where the marine base was situated. On my first visit in June 1945 I had flown the Bv 138 before flying the huge Bv 222 in Norway, but now, in the latter half of July, I was back to sample some of the other flying-boat types, bolstered by the confidence of having coped with the mighty Wiking.

The elegant Dornier 24 on take-off.

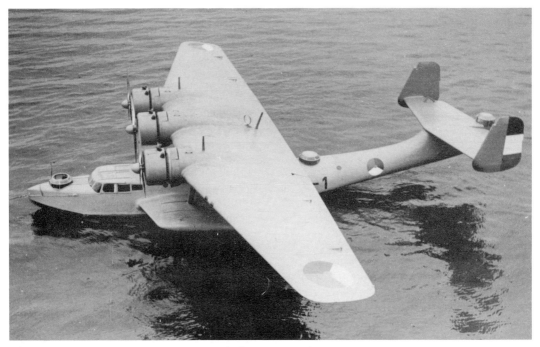

The magnificent Dornier 24 in service with the Royal Netherlands Naval Air Service.

The cockpit of the Dornier 24.

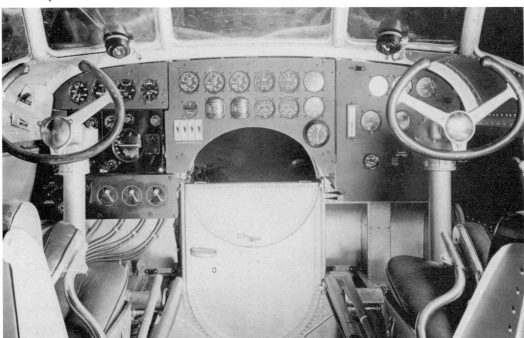

There was a most interesting collection of Dornier types, including the Do 18, Do 24 and Do 26 as well as the Bv 138. The order in which to fly them was dictated for me by my German pilot mentor, who waxed lyrical about the Do 24. Certainly I found his demonstration of its water capabilities truly astonishing, when instead of heading into wind along the Schlei he took the boat off in the inner basin by driving it round in a full circle until we picked up enough speed and hit our own wake to get lift-off.

The Do 24 was actually designed to meet a 1935 requirement of the Royal Netherlands Naval Air Service for operational duties in the Dutch East Indies. It was an all-metal flying-boat with a two-step hull and typical Dornier sponsons extending from the hull sides for lateral stability on the water. The three engines were carried on the centre section of the tapered wing, which was mounted above the hull and supported by inverted Vee struts and braced by sloping parallel struts to the sponsons. This was fundamentally the same wing structure as for the Do 18. Twin fins and rudders were carried on a braced tailplane mounted on the top of the upward-curving hull. The first flight was made on 3 July 1937.

Normally a crew of six was carried, comprising pilot, co-pilot/navigator, radio operator and three gunners. The gunners were in rotatable turrets located in the nose, tail and a dorsal position. The bow and tail turrets each had 1×7.9 mm MG 15 gun, and the dorsal turret had 1×20 mm MG 151 cannon. Twelve 50 kg (110 lb) bombs could also be carried. The span was 88 ft 7 ins, the length 72 ft 2 in, and the height 17 ft 10 in.

The Do 24 T-2 which I flew was powered by three 1,000 hp Bramo Fafnir 323R-2 9-cylinder air-cooled radial engines driving three-bladed controllable-pitch airscrews. Fuel was carried in the sponsons. Its empty weight was 20,286 lb and its loaded was 39,249lb.

The original Do 24Ks built for the Dutch were powered by 890 hp Wright R-1820-F52 Cyclone radial engines. After the occupation of Holland they were taken over by the Germans for air-sea rescue duties and redesignated the Do 24N-1.

The Do 24 control system was quite conventional, with slotted ailerons on the outer wing sections and split flaps on the centre section, statically and aerodynamically balanced rudders with servo flaps, and statically balanced elevators. All control surfaces were fabric-covered.

The cockpit was roomy and reasonably well laid out, but the view ahead was restricted by the rather long nose with the turret perched on top. Once the engines were started-up the cockpit noise level was quite high, but not oppressively so. Taxying was surprisingly easy by judicious use of the three engines available, and the manoeuvrability on the water gave confidence. However, I was hardly prepared for the incredible demonstration of this manoeuvrability on take-off, when my German check pilot opened up the engines to full power and, instead of running straight, started ruddering the boat round in a gentle circle, during which it remained beautifully stable laterally on its sponsons. Before we got up on the step the boat assumed a steep nose-up attitude, giving a very poor view ahead, but once on the step that attitude decreased markedly and acceleration improved until unstick occurred at 115 km/h (71.5 mph). Through-out take-off 15 degrees of flap were used.

The initial rate of climb after retraction of the flaps was a stately 500 ft/min but the Do 24 impressed with its comfortable feel arising from positive stability around all three axes, and effective controls. In the cruise at 3,000 ft at an airspeed of 295 km/h (183 mph), I found the harmony of control to be very good and the stick forces were not high for such a large aircraft. With a top speed of 340 km/h (211 mph), this performance was useful in enabling the Do 24 to get to the incident area in its air-sea rescue-role fairly smartly.

With a normal range of 1,800 miles, and a maximum range of 2,050 miles, this was an effective reconnaissance flying-boat. It was equipped for long flights with autopilot and sleeping bunks for the crew.

The great asset of the Do 24 for air-sea rescue was its ability to take-off and alight with relative ease in the open sea in fairly rough weather. The approach was made normally at 130 km/h (81 mph) with full flap, the centre engine throttled back and rate of descent controlled on the two outer engines. Very little change of attitude was required for hold-off, and touchdown occurred at 122 km/h (76 mph).

I made several flights in the Do 24N during July, September and October 1945, and was able to experiment with its asymmetric abilities. It could be flown comfortably on any two of the three engines, and in the event of the loss of two engines could be safely landed on the one remaining engine in sea state 5.

To me, the Do 24 was virtually viceless, and I certainly never met a German or Dutch pilot who had anything but praise for it. Although it was mainly used for SAR work, it was used by the Dutch for armed reconnaissance and was fitted with underwing racks to carry 12×110 lb bombs. Although Dornier played little part in the subsequent life of the Do 24, it certainly produced a winner in the initial development of a superb flying-boat.

The Do 24 in flight.

Chapter 19
Douglas AD-4 Skyraider

The original Skyraider was known as the Dauntless II, and the prototype was designated the XBT2D. The design was the brainchild of the great Ed Heinemann in June 1944, and it had a gestation period of less than nine months before the first flight on 18th March 1945.

The XBT2D was a single-seat, low-wing, naval attack cantilever monoplane with a span of 50 ft and a gross wing area of 400 ft². The thick wing gave a maximum lift coefficient of 2.0, and had all-metal ailerons with trim and balance tabs and Fowler-type trailing-edge flaps. The fuselage was an all-metal monocoque structure with a length of 38 ft 10½ in, with an integral fin giving it a height of 12 ft. Dive brakes were fitted, one on each side of the fuselage and one below. The tail unit had all-metal control surfaces with an electrically controlled adjustable tailplane. The rudder and elevator were aerodynamically and statically balanced, and trim and spring tabs were fitted on the rudder. A tailwheel was fitted for simplicity and weight saving.

The engine was an 18-cylinder air-cooled radial Wright R-3350-24W of 2,400 hp with a single-stage, two-speed supercharger,

The versatile AD-1 Skyraider.

The AD-3W Airborne Early Warning version of the Skyraider.

driving a 13½ ft four-bladed, constant speed, variable pitch hydraulic propeller. A single 380 US gallon self-sealing fuel tank was situated in the fuselage just behind the pilot. Armament consisted of 2×20 mm wing cannon, and the aircraft could be fitted with rocket launchers, bomb racks or torpedoes. Its empty weight was 10,470 lb.

The first flight by test pilot Laverne Browne was uneventful, but the subsequent programme of demonstration flights to the limits of the flight envelope as required by the US Navy ran into quite a few problem areas. There was particular trouble with the terminal dive and high 'g' pull-out, because the conditions laid down by the Bureau of Aeronautics put the aircraft into the unexpected effects of compressibility at a Mach number of 0.75. These tests were carried out on the first production aeroplane, designated the AD-1 Skyraider, which did not differ funda-

mentally from the prototype XBT2D.

The AD-1 entered fleet service on 6th December 1946, and in its numerous variants it served with the US Navy for 23 years. The most common model was the AD-4, which differed from earlier models in having the more powerful 2,700 hp R-3350-26 WA Double Cyclone engine, a redesigned windshield and cockpit enclosure to provide greater pilot protection, the addition of a P-1 automatic pilot and the installation of AN/APS-19A radar and Mark 3 Modification 3 bomb director.

The AD-4 carried a formidable load of armament consisting of 4×20 mm wing cannon, 12×5 in rockets plus 3×2,000 lb bombs or 3×Mark 13-3 torpedoes. The all-up weight with one 2,000 lb bomb was 16,850 lb, and the maximum AUW was an astonishing 23,716 lb.

The main change to the earlier controls

was that the ailerons were of the pressure balance type and hydraulically power-boosted at an 18:1 ratio with manual reversion. The three variable-position dive-brakes were hydraulically operated. The bomb displacing gear at the centreline station was powder operated by a standard engine starter cartridge.

The AD-4 was a really nice aircraft to handle, the only complaints I could level at it with regard to stability and control being the rather high stick force per 'g' and the constant directional retrimming required with changes in power and airspeed, although the trimmers on all control surfaces were very effective.

Very steep dives could be undertaken with this aircraft because the dive brakes were particularly effective. Their extension took $3\frac{1}{2}$ sec and gave a very slight nose-up change of trim, good deceleration and no buffet.

The aircraft was fitted with an artificial stall warning stick shaker, because otherwise there was virtually no aerodynamic stall warning other than increasing left wing heaviness before the wing actually dropped at the stall. Pre-stall warning is of course vital for carrier aircraft, whose landing approaches are made at very small increments of speed above the stall speed.

The Skyraider was an easy aircraft to deck land, and even with boost off the lateral control was satisfactory for this demanding task. The only slight criticism that could be levelled at the AD-4 for carrier work was the strong directional swing on take-off or wave-off, especially if power was applied rapidly. For carrier stowage the aircraft had a folded span of 23 ft $10\frac{1}{2}$ in and height of 16 ft 8 in. It had a top speed of 279 knots TAS at 18,300 ft, and its time to climb was 4 min to 10,000 ft and 9.6 min to 20,000 ft. The service ceiling was 32,200 ft and the range 780 nm at 175 knots TAS at 15,000 ft.

There is no doubt that the AD-4 Skyraider was an outstanding attack aircraft as regards weight lifting capacity, performance and handling characteristics.

Many variants of the Skyraider were built, and it must surely rank as one of the most useful general purpose aircraft ever built.

In parallel with the later models of the standard attack Skyraider, a special version was developed and built for airborne early warning and anti-submarine search duties. The first such model was the AD-3W, fitted with a large glassfibre radome approximately 8 ft wide, 12 ft long and 3 ft deep under the front fuselage and wing centre section, housing the search AEW antenna. An inverter housing was positioned behind the pilot's cockpit enclosure, and two radar operators sat in the rear fuselage. No armament or dive brakes were fitted, and the fuel tanks were housed in the wings. These modifications reduced the aircraft's overall length by $5\frac{1}{2}$ in and increased the folded height to 17 ft 8 in. The normal AUW was 16,877 lb.

It was soon apparent that the directional stability had greatly deteriorated from that of the basic AD owing to the large radome, so two auxiliary fins were added to the tailplane on each side of the main fin and rudder. The stalling characteristics had also been adversely affected, displaying a 45 degrees left wing drop in the landing configuration, and an abrupt 90 degrees left wing drop in the power approach configuration. The landing configuration stall was improved by fitting a V-type spoiler on the leading edge of the right-hand inboard wing, but slats had to be installed on the leading edge of both outboard wings to bring the power approach stall to an acceptable standard.

The basic AD was spun in all configurations, and also carrying a 2,000 lb bomb, and the spin characteristics and recovery were normal, the latter requiring no more than half a turn. However, the AD-3W's spin was flat and rudder overbalance occurred in the direction of the spin, so recovery on test had to be made by deploying the anti-spin parachute. In its wisdom, the US Navy decided to settle for the prohibition of spinning in the W models.

An AEW Skyraider of the
Royal Navy.

The AD-4W was the radome-equipped version of the AD-4. The only significant change in the handling characteristics was a right wing dropping tendency just after touchdown on landing, and an attendant tendency to swerve to the right during the landing run. These peculiarities were attributable to the effect of the spoiler, and were annoying but not dangerous.

Performance figures of the AD-4W gave the expected speed and range decreases, but surprisingly showed slight improvements in climb. The top speed was 242 knots TAS at 18,000 ft. Time to climb was 3.9 min to 10,000 ft and 9.1 min to 20,000 ft. The service ceiling was 32,900 ft, and the range 740 nm at 130 knots TAS at 1,500 ft.

The AD-4W filled a much-needed AEW requirement for the US Fleet and it complemented the attack AD-4 perfectly at a crisis time – the Korean War, where the AD-4 played a key role in disrupting North Korean lines of communication, and where its low-level operations kept it relatively immune from MiG fighters but not from anti-aircraft fire, though it proved it could take heavy punishment and survive.

The AD-4W found its way into the Royal Navy when about forty were supplied in late 1951 under the Mutual Defence Assistance Programme. After intensive operational training they were grouped into a front-line unit, No 849 Squadron with its Headquarters Flight at Culdrose in Cornwall, and with four operational Flights (A,B,C and D), each of four aircraft for detachment as separate units to aircraft carriers at sea.

The desire to improve the AD-4W was reflected in its development, the AD-5W, which eliminated the fixed slats, spoiler, and the additional tail fins. This was achieved by a 56 per cent increase in fin and rudder area, although the AD-6W reverted to the AD-4W configuration.

In some ways the Skyraider reminded me of the old Swordfish – almost an anachronism but incredibly versatile, and truly an aircraft for all seasons. The Swordfish was a great weight lifter, but the Skyraider was prodigious in this respect, and is known to have lifted 10,500 lb of bombs on a flight made in 1954. Both aircraft had a profound effect on the wars in which they were engaged, and their battle honours bear testament to their enduring qualities.

Chapter 20
Douglas F3D-2 Skyknight

One of my first projects as a test pilot in Flight Test at Patuxent River Naval Air Test Center in 1951 was the F3D-2 Skyknight, a mid-wing naval night fighter carrying two crew seated side-by-side. It was big for a carrier-borne aircraft, having a wing span of 50 ft, a length of 45 ft 6 in and an all-up weight of 24,569 lb, with a maximum weight of 26,750 lb.

This large aeroplane was powered by two 3,400 lb static thrust axial flow J34-WE-36 turbo-jets, and had an internal fuel capacity of 1,350 US gallons. Armament was 4×20 mm under-nose cannon and 2×1,000 lb bombs carried externally, but the external store arrangement was being modified to permit carriage of 4×2,000 lb air-to-air missiles.

The main changes made in the F3D-2 compared with the F3D-1 were:

a The thrust of the engines was increased by 150 lb each.

b Elimination of the under-fuselage speed brake, which gave excessive nose-down pitch on extension, and increase of the opening angle of the side-fuselage, variable-position speed brakes from 45 to 55 degrees to improve effectiveness.

c The force exerted by the elevator downspring was reduced through a change in the bell-crank system when the speed brakes were extended, thus reducing longitudinal trim changes.

d Aileron spoilers were fitted on the upper surface of each wing forward of the wing flap, and were hydraulically actuated by pressure from the aileron power boost system. Both spoilers remained closed until the control stick was moved past approximately 8 degrees either side of neutral. Since the boost system pressure was proportional to stick force, the spoiler angle depended on stick force and the aerodynamic hinge force on the spoiler. Full spoiler opening was obtained with a 30 lb stick force at the maximum indicated airspeed. The spoiler was closed as the control stick passed the 8 degrees position on its return towards neutral. This modification was made to improve the boost-on rate of roll of the F3D-1, which was a maximum of 98 degrees per second at 265 knots.

e The Pioneer P-1 autopilot was replaced by a G-3 autopilot, which provided automatic yaw damping to increase yaw stability during manual flight. During manually controlled turns the rudder was automatically co-ordinated by the yaw damper. If an unco-ordinated turn, such as a sideslip, was to be made with the yaw damper engaged, the pilot had to overpower the rudder.

f The ailerons were still hydraulically power-boosted at a 20:1 ratio, but now had manual reversion which incorporated a spring-loaded mechanical advantage shifter. When the power-boost system failed the shifter then became effective automatically and reduced aileron travel to half the normal travel, therefore halving the required stick forces. The earlier F3D-1 aircraft did not have this advantage shifter, but instead the control stick could be extended three inches by pressing a button below the pilot's hand grip to offer better leverage to combat the high manual forces.

Taxying the Skyknight was very straightforward, but take-off acceleration was poor and the distance rather long. The

The chivalrous F3D-2 Skyknight night fighter.

unstick at 100 knots was clean, but the climb thereafter was pedestrian, requiring 34 min to reach the service ceiling of 36,800 ft.

In general, the longitudinal stability and control of this aircraft were satisfactory except for the high manoeuvring control forces (18 lb per 'g' at 400 knots at 10,000 ft at mid-centre of gravity).

Lateral stick free stability was negative and the ailerons did not self-centre. This was a bad feature for instrument flying, and could be partly attributed to the high aileron control break-out forces, which were of the order of 4 lb. Rate of roll was 110 degrees per sec at 260 knots.

The aircraft snaked badly at speeds in excess of 150 knots and Dutch rolled at lower speeds without the yaw damper in operation, but in each case operation with the yaw damper engaged was satisfactory. However, care had to be taken in engaging the mechanism, ensuring that the pilot's feet were off the rudder pedals, as it started the rudder pulsing immediately on engagement, and if the pilot's feet were holding the pedals then the action of the yaw damper was momentarily resisted. Thus the rudder was thrown out of phase in its movement to counteract the aircraft's yawing motion, which as a result was momentarily aggravated and could cause large angles of sideslip at high speeds.

For strafing and gunnery runs the yaw damper had certain disadvantages. In a strafing run it was excellent, provided the pilot found himself in a true line-up on his target in his dive, but if for any reason he was off line and had to correct by over-powering the yaw damper by manual application of the rudder pedals, he usually aggravated a yawing condition which he might not have time to let the yaw damper re-correct once he was on his new target line.

In air-to-air gunnery runs the same feature was present, and it was also noticeable that on entering any turn the yaw damper initially applied insufficient rudder to give a co-ordinated turn, although it corrected this situation once the turn was stabilised.

The G-3 autopilot, besides incorporating a yaw damper, had a small manoeuvring stick, a leveller button which when pushed returned the aircraft to level flight from any attitude of climb, glide or bank up to 65 degrees, and a constant barometric altitude maintain button. It was a most satisfactory autopilot in flight, and its installation was neat.

The first signs of compressibility effects occurred at M=0.80 when buffeting started, accompanied by mild alternate wing dropping and a nose-up trim change, all of which characteristics intensified up to a safe flight Mach number limit of 0.84. The solid speed brakes were rather ineffective and gave a lot of buffet at full extension. If extended at M=0.82 they gave no change of trim and took about 5 sec to open fully.

The F3D-2 stall gave no aerodynamic warning other than a slight airframe tremor about 2 knots before the left wing dropped abruptly, so an artificial stick shaker warning device was an essential fitting. Accelerated stalls were characterised by some 10 knots stick-shaker warning before a mild roll-off occurred to the left. With the stick shaker disconnected a very gentle airframe tremor could be felt about 5 knots before the stall.

The deck landing characteristics of the Skyknight were magnificent, except that there was an annoying cockpit buffet with the top access hatch open. The deck landing approach speed was 100 knots at a normal landing weight of 20,000 lb, although the aircraft was cleared for arrested landings at weights up to 22,600 lb. Its folded span was 22 ft 10 in, and folded height 16 ft 6 in.

Boost-off lateral control was satisfactory for deck landing the F3D-2, the rate of roll under these conditions being 30 degrees per second for a 30 lb stick force. This boost-off rate of roll was more than double that of the F3D-1.

In September 1951, with the blessing of the British Admiralty, I had handed over to the US Navy the concept of the angled deck. Its potential was at once realised, and by the spring of next year NATC Patuxent River was carrying out field power-on landing trials, which were inherent in the angled deck concept of operations. These field trials were extended to shipboard evaluation on the USS *Wasp* on 2nd March 1952. Thereafter the field carrier landing practice was intensified in preparation for trials aboard a carrier with an 8 degree angled deck painted on the existing flight deck.

During this stage of the trials I was allocated an F3D-2, although also assigned to the F9F-5 Panther and F2H-2 Banshee groups. The test involved 16 pilots, four being squadron pilots and the remainder NATC pilots. The trials took place on the USS *Midway* on 27th May 1952, and were completely successful.

The single-engine flight handling characteristics of the F3D-2 were good, but single-engine performance was weak. With the undercarriage lowered and flaps lowered one quarter and a low fuel weight (about 2,000 lb), a single-engine deck landing could be made at 115 knots, and a wave-off taken provided the undercarriage was retracted at once.

The top speed of the aircraft was 453 knots TAS at 14,000 ft, and its range was 1,170 nm at 350 knots TAS at 30,000 ft. While I was at NATC the Douglas company had reported that preliminary tests with the slope of the jet tailpipes reduced from 12 to 7 degrees showed a substantial increase in performance.

No ejection seat was fitted in the Skyknight, and bale-out arrangements were inadequate for any accelerated flight condition. On the credit side, however, the cockpit lighting was excellent, being of the latest state-of-the-art type.

My summing-up of the F3D-2 was that the very second-rate performance,

A Skyknight operated by the US Navy in the Korean War.

particularly with regards to rate of climb and acceleration, ruined what was a potentially fine night fighter. It is difficult to conceive why virtually the same engines as fitted to the F2H-2 Banshee should have been chosen for this much larger and heavier aircraft. The service ceiling could not be achieved on a full-power climb from sea level without exceeding the maximum allowable continuous engine running time at 100 per cent rpm.

Undoubtedly the F3D-2 was one of the most comfortable aircraft I have ever flown, and was remarkably short of flight handling deficiencies if one assumes the correct functioning of such auxiliary devices as the autopilot and artificial stall warning. However, unless something drastic was done to step up the engine thrust available it could never meet its operational specification.

The F3D-1 was never deployed in squadron strength aboard ship. The F3D-2, however, was used extensively by the Marines as a night fighter in Korea, and eventually became the only fighter to serve in combat in both Korea and Vietnam, finally retiring from the Marines in 1970.

Chapter 21
Douglas F4D-1 Skyray

Soon after I arrived at the US Naval Air Test Center, Patuxent River, in the capacity of Resident British Test Pilot in September 1951, the crew room conversation invariably turned to the Korean War and what the US Navy was doing to combat the MiG menace. Much faith was being pinned on the North American FJ-2 Fury, a development from the USAF F-86E Sabre, and on the Douglas F4D-1 Skyray, which had made its first flight on 23rd January 1951.

The prototype XF4D-1 was a delta-wing, single-seat naval interceptor fighter powered by a 7,400 lb static thrust axial flow J40-WE-8 turbojet, to be fitted with an afterburner to increase the thrust to 10,900 lb. Its span was 33 ft 6 in, length 44 ft, and height 14 ft 3 in, and its folded span for carrier storage was 25 ft 6 in. The all-up weight was 18,030 lb. The armament comprised 4×20 mm wing cannon or four rocket launchers, each capable of carrying six folding-fin stabilised rockets. Internal fuel capacity was 640 US gallons.

The delta wing had 52½ degrees leading edge sweepback, and longitudinal and

The prototype XF4D-1 Skyray.

The delta Skyray shipborne fighter.

lateral control was by means of irreversible hydraulically powered elevons. There were inboard and outboard elevon control surfaces on each wing, and they were normally latched together and acted symmetrically for elevator control and asymmetrically for aileron control. Artificial spring feel was to be provided on production models. In the event of hydraulic system failure, the fluid trapped in the elevon actuating cylinders by the control valves held the elevons in the control position prevailing at the time of the hydraulic failure, even though the aerodynamic force was too great for the pilot to overcome. Moving the stick in a direction concurring with the aerodynamic loads permitted release of the trapped fluid; the outboard elevons, being mechanically connected to the pilot's stick, were then operated manually to provide control. The inboard elevons, being uncontrolled, were free to float. At low speeds and at high speeds in level flight, where aerodynamic forces are low, the changeover to manual control was instantaneous. The pilot's stick could be extended in the cockpit to increase the mechanical advantage when operating the control manually.

A trimmer surface was installed on each wing inboard of each inboard elevon to provide additional longitudinal control for take-off or landing under normal operation, and to serve as an emergency pull-out device if the elevon power system failed. These pitch trimmers were electrically operated by a thumb switch on the pilot's stick.

Wing leading edge slats were fitted and were actuated automatically by aerodynamic loads. Four small hydraulically actuated, variable-position speed brakes were also installed, one on the lower surface and one on the upper surface of each wing.

The rudder control was conventional, and a yaw stabilisation system was fitted which not only damped out directional oscillations but at low speeds provided additional rudder movement as required to co-ordinate a manoeuvre.

The foregoing describes the XF4D-1 as I encountered it. This prototype did not come to Patuxent River during my spell of duty there, but a NATC evaluation team was sent to the Douglas plant at El Segundo in California in May 1952 to fly the aircraft, and I was fortunate enough to accompany them. I was impressed by the look of the Skyray – neat and smooth but suggesting lethal potential, although we had been advised that it had problem areas. The cockpit was surprisingly roomy, but the layout of switches did not seem inspired by any obvious pattern of logic.

Taxying was easy and the take-off acceleration quite good provided the engine was run up on the brakes, although a positive pull was required to unstick the aircraft at 100 knots. The climb rate was disappointing and decidedly in need of the boost from an afterburner, since it took 19 min to reach 40,000 ft. This lack of power was also evident in a maximum speed run at 40,000 ft, which only clocked 520 knots true air speed.

Longitudinal stability and control were satisfactory up to Mach=0.92, except for extremely high control sensitivity near neutral at high indicated airspeeds. The use of the pitch trimmers as trim devices and as an aid to longitudinal control was considered unsatisfactory because of their ineffectiveness.

The high 'g' buffet boundary was one of the most outstanding features of the aircraft. At 40,000 ft a steady acceleration of 3.4 g could be pulled at M=0.90 without airframe buffet, and at 30,000 ft at M=0.80 a steady 4g could be obtained.

Stick force per 'g' varied from 4½ lb at 350 knots at 10,000 ft at mid CG to 12 lb at 175 knots and 35 lb in the landing configuration

at 120 knots. This latter figure was, of course, very excessive.

Static lateral stability was strong at high speeds, and increased as speed was reduced, becoming excessively strong for the landing approach. Lateral control effectiveness was also marginal for landing, but increased with speed until it became exceptionally high at higher indicated airspeeds, where it was extremely sensitive near neutral stick position. Manual reversion control gave very large forces which required the pilot to use both hands during the landing approach. Since the control forces appeared to increase linearly with speed, the aircraft would probably have been unmanageable at high speeds in this condition.

Without the yaw damper operating, directional stability was unsatisfactory at low speeds. The yaw stabilisation system fitted to the prototype did not sufficiently damp lateral directional oscillations, but the production aircraft was to incorporate a two-piece rudder, split chordwise, with one section acting as a damper and the other as a rudder surface. Both sections would tend to move as a unit unless an adverse yaw signal was transmitted by the yaw damper, thus allowing the pilot to feel rudder forces and position feed-back passed through the rudder pedals by the action of the yaw damper when a single surface was used.

High-frequency rudder oscillations were encountered above M=0.92 which necessitated locking the rudder mechanically before attaining that Mach number. The aircraft had not been flown in excess of M=0.95 with the rudder locked, because the drag rise at that Mach number became abrupt with small transonic trim changes, and it seemed unlikely that the XF4D-1 would be able to achieve sonic speed with the thrust available. The speed brakes gave excess buffet above 300 knots, ineffective deceleration, and a very slight nose-down trim change.

The stall characteristics were good, light

buffet starting at 13 knots before the stall and increasing in intensity until a wing drop occurred at 95 knots at an AUW of 15,810 lb with the aircraft in the powered landing approach configuration. The minimum trim speed, however, was too high, so that with full nose-up trimmer setting a pull force of 25 lb was required to reach the stall.

The view for deck-landing was very good at an approach speed of 115 knots, when the angle of incidence was 15.7 degrees. Below this speed the control on the approach deteriorated owing to a sharp increase in drag with increase in attitude, reduced lateral control, and increased dihedral effect. At a speed of 107 knots and an incidence of 18 degrees the view was acceptable, but at 100.5 knots and 20 degrees it was unsatisfactory. Under such conditions the poor engine acceleration characteristics made a wave-off critical.

The XF4D-1 was really in too early a stage of development to allow us to arrive at any final conclusions, but it showed promise which would need an afterburner to fulfil it. It was unlikely to find itself suited to the environment of the Korean War because of its short range, if indeed its development problems did not exclude it from that conflict because of the time scale. These were the views of the evaluation team, and they proved to be prophetic.

The Skyray was given a boost when the XF4D-1 set a world speed record of 753 mph (1212 km/h) over a 3 km (1.86-mile) course on 3rd October 1953, flown by a naval pilot, but by this time the Korean War was effectively over.

The problem-plagued XJ40 engine was the primary cause of the F4D-1's delayed entry into squadron service. This took place on 16th April 1956, and its limited operational success saw it finally withdrawn in February 1964.

The concept of the delta-wing Skyray filled the US Navy with the hope of a bright new star on its horizon, but sadly it never realised its potential and gradually dimmed into relative mediocrity. It was just another casualty in the post Second World War era of innovatory aviation technology inspired by the advanced state of the art in defeated Germany.

Chapter 22
Focke-Wulf Ta 154

One of the interesting tasks I had to perform on behalf of the RAE Farnborough in the immediate post Second World War months was to scour Germany and its former occupied territories for the more unusual types of Luftwaffe aircraft. On one such tour of northwest Germany in my trusty Siebel 204, I landed at Jever on the south bank of the river Elbe on 25 October 1945, and was told that a visit to the airfield at Stade might be worth my while, as the RAF Regiment had listed an unidentified type amongst the aircraft found there.

I flew over to Stade in the afternoon and found the usual collection of wrecks waiting for disposal, plus three semi-serviceable ones awaiting survey by authorities such as the RAE. Two were Focke-Wulf FW 190s, but the third was a rare Ta 154, and it looked in such a reasonable state that I got the local British Army unit to tell me where I might find some Luftwaffe POWs who could advise me if it was flyable. The Army excelled itself, and said they could produce some civilian engineers from the Focke-Wulf works at Bremen, who were now

The Ta 154 V1 prototype, Kurt Tank's answer to the dreaded British Mosquito.

incarcerated in a barracks some 15 miles distant. By mid-afternoon they were on the airfield, and were told that if they worked overnight to try and make the aircraft serviceable they would receive some improvements to their diet.

The Ta 154 had been built to meet a German Air Ministry specification issued in September 1942 for a night fighter antidote to the ubiquitous Mosquito, and as a counterpart to the Heinkel He 219, the development of which had been badly delayed by the Allied bombing campaign and which was obviously not in the performance class to deal with the British raider. At that time Germany had a shortage of strategic metals and metalworkers, but an abundance of wood and skilled woodworkers, so the Air Ministry decided that the new aircraft would be mainly of wooden construction.

Focke-Wulf proposed a twin-engined, two-seat shoulder-winged aeroplane with a tricycle undercarriage, to have the unofficial name of Moskito! It actually flew just nine months later, on 1st July 1943, piloted by its designer, Kurt Tank. I was fortunate enough to have interrogated Kurt Tank just after the war ended, and although the Ta 154 was only of passing interest, he had talked enthusiastically of the maiden flight. He felt he had taken on a very challenging commitment with the wooden construction of the Ta 154, but considered that at least he had no competitor, as the only alternatives open to the Air Ministry were to develop the He 219 or Junkers Ju 388J. Certainly his forebodings were well founded, because the bonding agent used for the wood was produced by a firm which was bombed out of existence, and the replacement agents proved unsatisfactory and resulted in the break-up in the air of the first two production Ta 154A-1s. Tank took it upon himself to stop production until the problem was solved, and for his pains was called to appear before a tribunal in Nuremberg, accused of sabotaging the war

effort. *Reichsmarschall* Goering himself arraigned Tank, but a reprimand only was the outcome.

However, the die was cast, and official cancellation of the Ta 154 came before the end of 1944. Seven of the Ta 154A-1 night fighters under construction at the time were completed and used operationally at Stade in 1945.

Besides the intact machine at Stade there were two in a rather sorry state, but they were a potential source of spares. On 26th October I arrived at the airfield to find the Ta 154 standing outside the hangar with its engines running, and I was able to make my first real visual assessment of this interesting aeroplane. It looked very sleek, with an extremely shallow front fuselage with the cockpit fairing flush with the upper surface of the wings, and generally somewhat more diminutive than the British Mosquito. Only the huge nosewheel looked out of proportion; otherwise its lines were enhanced by the tricycle layout and the mighty engines.

The German mechanics were obviously pleased with themselves for getting the engines going. They were reasonably happy about the electrics, but much less so about the hydraulics. They refused blankly to declare the aircraft '*flugklar*' (cleared to fly), and voiced their particular concern about the type's history of crashes, not only due to the faulty wood bonding but also because there had been a lot of trouble with the nosewheel failing to lower properly. My mood was one of frustration at that point, but I decided to let off steam by at least taxying the aircraft.

The crew sat in tandem in the cockpit, with the radio/radar operator sitting behind the pilot and facing forward. The cockpit was very heavily armoured and the layout was neat and logical, but the view was bad sideways and downwards, although this was possibly acceptable in a night fighter.

The Ta 154A-1 had a wing span of 52 ft 6 in and length of 39 ft 8⅜ in. It was powered by two 1,500 hp Junkers Jumo 2llR 12-

cylinder inverted Vee liquid-cooled engines with annular nose radiators, driving three-bladed fully-feathering airscrews. The fuel capacity was 330 Imperial gallons, housed in two tanks aft of the crew accommodation. Armament was 1×30 mm MK 108 and 1×20 mm MG 151 cannon on each side of the forward fuselage, and there was provision for a 30 mm cannon mounted at a forward angle of 45 degrees to fire from the top of the rear fuselage. The empty weight was 14,123 lb, and the loaded weight 18,191 lb. The control surfaces were metal-framed and fabric covered, the rudder being horn-balanced and having a servo tab which also acted as a trimmer. The elevators were mass-balanced, and the tailplane was adjustable. The wings had ailerons and variable-camber, slotted flaps. The main undercarriage wheels retracted rearwards into the engine nacelles, while the nose-wheel turned through 90 degrees as it retracted rearwards to lie flat in the fuselage.

The aircraft taxied easily and the engines sounded very healthy, so, with curiosity rapidly overcoming discretion, I threw caution to the winds and decided to make a quick take-off, circuit and landing as the weather was fine. I left the wheels down because the feel of the brakes convinced me that all was not well with the hydraulics.

The take-off run without flaps was about 600 m on grass, and with the excellent acceleration the nosewheel could be raised at 80 mph, unstick following at 100 mph. The climb with wheels down was surprisingly good up to 2,000 ft, where I levelled off to avoid overheating the engines. I then made a couple of circuits to check stability and control at the very limited speed possible. Stability was positive around all three axes, and harmony of control was impressive, while the effectiveness of all controls was satisfactory at such low speed. According to what I had learned from Kurt Tank, this situation apertained throughout the whole

speed and altitude range of the aircraft, and I had no reason to disbelieve that.

For landing I reduced height to 1,000 ft and made a normal landing pattern, with flaps being lowered at 150 mph and the final approach speed reduced to 120 mph. I crossed the threshold at 115 mph and touched down at 105 mph. The nosewheel could be held off on the landing run down to 70 mph, which was just as well as the brakes were decidedly shaky. Indeed, I did not even attempt to taxi back to the hangar, but vacated the aircraft where it stood after shutting down the engines. Obviously there was little point in recommending that the Ta 154 be taken back to RAE for flight testing, and I believe it only got a cursory visit from our armament experts.

In 1960, when I was seconded to Focke-Wulf at Bremen as their test pilot for six months at the instigation of the German government, I was quite fascinated to find that they had recovered many of their wartime files, and they gave me free access to these records. There I dug out the handling reports and performance data on the Ta 154A-1, which showed its potential. With the Jumo 211R engines the maximum speed was 430 mph at 20,000 ft, and thus it had the edge on the Mosquito, but the predicted top speed with the later intended Jumo 213Es of 1,750 hp was a whopping 465 mph at 32,000 ft. Rate of climb was 2,300 ft/min, service ceiling was 36,000 ft, range 1,000 miles, and maximum endurance 2¾ hr. (For convenience all the speeds and heights have been converted from metric values).

On the basis of a 15 min flight of a very restricted nature I am hardly qualified to pass judgement on the Ta 154, but this limited experience, combined with my high opinion of Focke-Wulf as a company and Kurt Tank as a designer, leads me to believe that it was a potentially formidable aeroplane thwarted by a technical problem outside the scope of aviation technology at a critical time in its development. *Sic gloria transit!*

Chapter 23
Grumman AF-2 Guardian

The Guardian was originally conceived by Grumman as a replacement for the excellent Avenger torpedo bomber, and as originally projected in 1944 was a composite-powered aeroplane. The XTB3F was a mid-wing design with a 2,300 hp Pratt & Whitney R-2800-46 Double Wasp engine in the nose. In place of defensive armament this prototype had a Westinghouse 19XB turbojet in the tail to give it a high escape speed. It made its first flight on 19th December 1945, but tests soon revealed the inadequacy of the jet boost for its intended function, and it was eliminated.

Production models were ordered in two configurations; the radar-equipped AF-2W and the weapon-carrying AF-2S. The AF-2S was a mid-wing, three-crew anti-submarine attack aircraft carrying AN/APS31 radar under the starboard wing and an AVQ-2 searchlight under the port wing. The AF-2W was a four-crew anti-submarine search aircraft, carrying APS-20A antennae and radome under its fuselage.

These two types of aircraft normally operated together to form a hunter-killer combination. The AF-2W detected underwater craft and directed its companion

The radar-equipped Grumman AF-2W Guardian.

The hunter-killer team of AF-2W and AF-2S Guardians.

aircraft on to the target, whereupon the AF-2S laid down a pattern of sonobuoys to determine the exact location of the enemy submarine, and then launched its sonic-directed torpedo to complete the attack. Rockets could be carried to augment the torpedo.

For a single-engine aircraft the Guardian was large, with a span of 60 ft, a length of 42 ft 10 in and a height of 16 ft 9 in. The normal AUW was 20,430 lb (-2S) and 19,590 lb (-2W), with maximums of 22,640 lb (-2S) and 21,800 lb (-2W).

The Double Wasp engine had a single-stage, single-speed supercharger, and gave a top speed of 236 knots at 4,000 ft with a range of 985 nm at 135 knots at sea level for the -2S, the -2W's range being 40 nm less.

Spring tabs were fitted to the ailerons and elevators. The lateral control system included flaperons and flaperettes, which were auxiliary control surfaces hinged to the wing upper surface, designed to decrease adverse yaw and increase rate of roll. The flaperons were two rectangular flaps attached to the wing surfaces at their leading edges by hinges, and located one on each outboard panel forward of the outboard flap and inboard of the ailerons. The flaperettes consisted of two small rectangular flaps, each of which was attached by hinges at the leading edge to the flaperon upper surface near the flaperon trailing edge. The flaperons and flaperettes were hydraulically powered, and each assembly was raised in conjunction with upward travel of the adjacent aileron. After ½ in of stick travel from neutral the flaperette started opening to a maximum position of 90 degrees from the flaperon surface. Continued stick motion elevated the flaperon trailing edge to a maximum position of 40 degrees from the wing surface. In the event of boost failure there was manual reversion. The rudder was hydraulically power-boosted at a 4:1 ratio, and had manual reversion in conjunction with the flaperons.

The cockpit was very roomy and well laid out, with good all-round view. In spite of this, taxying was not easy because the hydraulic wheel brakes were inadequate for the large mass of this aircraft, and tended to overheat and become useless.

The take-off was a lumbering affair, but with a surprisingly short run and an initial rate of climb of just over 2,000 ft/min. However, this was essentially a low-level aeroplane, and did not even have an oxygen system fitted.

In general, the longitudinal stability characteristics of this aircraft were satisfactory. The stick force per 'g' was high (16 lb/'g' at 200 knots at 5,000 ft at mid CG), except in snatch pull-outs, particularly at speeds in excess of 300 knots, when it lightened off dangerously. In view of the nature of the aircraft's mission these characteristics could be accepted.

Lateral control forces were moderately high, but the rate of roll (about 40 degrees/sec) was adequate for the aircraft's functional duty. With boost off, lateral stick forces increased slightly and the rate of roll was about halved, but was still adequate for deck landing.

Harmony of control was poor. Weak lateral and strong directional control force stability combined to make it difficult to co-ordinate the controls in manoeuvring flight and in rough air. Inertia forces were also high.

The stall in all configurations lacked any aerodynamic warning and consisted of a sharp right-wing drop. Because of this an artificial stall warning stick shaker was fitted.

Movement of the flaps caused a large trim change (nose-down when lowering), but the low extension and retraction rate of the flaps allowed sufficient time to trim out the elevator control forces during transition. There was an undesirable cockpit buffet at landing approach speeds with the canopy open, but this could be eliminated by opening the cowl flaps more than halfway.

We conducted spinning trials at Naval Air Test Center, Patuxent River, and the test aircraft was fitted with an anti-spin parachute in a housing under the tail which extended aft of the rear fuselage extremity. Certainly the spin characteristics were only marginally acceptable with regard to recovery from the flattish rotation of the spin. Indeed, the boss of Flight Test, Lt-Col Marion Carl, had suspicions that the anti-spin parachute housing was, by virtue of its extra keel surface, favourably affecting the spin recovery, so he decided to find out for himself. On 1st April 1952 he took off in the AF-2S minus the anti-spin parachute gear, accompanied by me in an SNB-5 Expediter acting as chase plane. He climbed to 10,000 ft over Chesapeake Bay while I circled the test area at 6,000 ft.

At about 14.30 the Guardian entered a spin to the right, which was steep at first and then flattened. It passed our level after about three turns and continued in a stabilised spin attitude. I followed it down, expecting recovery at any moment, but it never came, so at about 3,000 ft I called for the pilot to eject. At about 1,000 ft there was no sign of recovery and no ejection by the pilot, but I could see him struggling to get out of the now open cockpit on the inside of the spin, which was the recommended method. Finally at 500 ft he got out on the outside of the spin, but I did not see his parachute open, and the aircraft spun into the water, leaving a huge white splash circle. This did not totally subside as the Guardian sank, and then I realised that I was looking at an open parachute canopy on the surface of the water. Then Marion's head appeared and he gave a frantic wave, so I radioed base to send a flying-boat at once. A P5M Mariner appeared within twenty minutes, and I circled low over him until he was rescued. Needless to say, the outcome was that intentional spinning of the Guardian was prohibited.

At the post-crash debrief Lt-Col Carl

revealed that he had tried to eject, but the face blind had pulled away completely in his hand. A wind tunnel investigation was also started on the best method of baling out manually from a spinning aircraft in the light of Carl's difficulties in getting out of the AF-2S.

Carrier trials with the Guardian in November 1950 had shown that it had much the same deck landing characteristics as its forebear, the Avenger, but revealed some small structural problems which necessitated redesign of the arrester hook attachment and the substitution of non-retractable dual tailwheels for the retractable single wheel. It was not an easy aircraft to handle on the deck, and even with its folded span of 26 ft 2 in looked immense in the hangar.

In general the Guardian was a good aircraft for its operational task, and its most noteworthy feature was the gain in rolling moment obtained from the flaperon and flaperette arrangement, although the resulting adverse yaw (10 degrees for full aileron deflection and with the rudder fixed when in the landing approach configuration) was rather high.

Chapter 24
Grumman F9F Panther

The Grumman Aircraft Engineering Corporation entered the field of jet aeroplane design in early 1946, when it responded to a US Navy request for proposals for a turbojet-powered all-weather shipboard fighter. Its submission, the XF9F-1, was a large side-by-side two-seater powered by four 1,500 lb static thrust Westinghouse J30 engines. However, installation difficulties, combined with the project's size and weight, led to its cancellation six months later, but Grumman had already turned its attention to a fresh design for a single-seat shipboard day fighter with alternative single- and twin-engine layouts using current Rolls-Royce types of jet engines. The US Navy favoured the single-engine design with the Rolls-Royce Nene of 5,000 lb static thrust, and three prototypes of the XF9F-2 were ordered in September 1946, the first and third powered by the Nene, and the second by a 4,600 lb Allison J33-A-8 and designated XF9F-3. The first flight of the XF9F-2 took place on 24th November 1947.

Pratt & Whitney had now negotiated a licensing arrangement to build the Nene, and this derivative was to power the

Grumman F9F-5 Panther on test at NATC, Patuxent River.

Grumman Panther being catapulted from US Navy aircraft carrier.

XF9F-5. The XF9F-4 was powered by an improved Allison J33, but the engine still gave difficulties.

From February 1948 detachable but non-jettisonable 120 US gallon wingtip tanks were flight-tested on the first XF9F-2, and were found to afford a useful endplate effect and improve aileron response as well as augmenting the capacity of the main fuel system. These tanks were to be standardised from the 13th production Panther.

The testing of the prototype Panther revealed a few problems, such as longi-tudinal stability at slow speed and marked directional snaking throughout the speed range. These led to enlargement of the vertical tail surfaces and the provision of baffles in the fuselage fuel tanks.

The first deliveries of the F9F-2 to an operational unit were made in May 1949, and in the next year it entered into combat

in the Korean War. Meanwhile, Grumman had turned its efforts to developing the Panther in the shape of the F9F-5, which first flew on 21st December 1949. This version was powered by the Pratt & Whitney J48-P-6 of 6,550 lb static thrust, and had a 19.5 in extension of the fuselage ahead of the wing to permit a very necessary increase in the capacity of the fuselage fuel tanks. The lengthening necessitated a further increase in vertical tail surface area to compensate for the resultant loss of directional stability.

The first F9F-5 was delivered to the US Naval Air Test Center at Patuxent River in January 1951, and I arrived there eight months later as the Resident British Naval Test Pilot attached to Flight Test Division. My first assignment was as Project Officer on the F9F-5, which was already in squadron service on a limited operational release, so my job was to fill in the gaps necessary to bring it up to full release status.

The first thing that struck me about the Panther was its sheer size by British standards. It had a span of 38 ft, a length of 38 ft 11 ins, an empty weight of 10,147 lb and a maximum weight of 20,965 lb. Although a somewhat portly aeroplane in the Grumman tradition, it had a certain appealing elegance. It housed a lot of fuel, carrying 1,003 US gallons, of which 240 US gallons were in the wingtip tanks, from which the fuel could be jettisoned in one minute at an airspeed of 340 knots. A pressure-operated water injection system was fitted, utilising a mixture of three parts distilled water with two parts alcohol, thus boosting the engine thrust to 7,000 lb. Armament consisted of 4×20 mm nose cannon, and 6×0.5 in rockets plus 2×1,000 lb bombs could be carried externally.

The Panther was a mid-wing design, with the engine buried in the fuselage and having an unusually short tailpipe below and forward of the tail unit. Both elevators had spring tabs with additional pilot controlled trim tabs. There were pilot operated trim tabs on the ailerons and rudder. The ailerons were hydraulically power-boosted at a 37:1 ratio, and had manual reversion in event of hydraulic failure.

The flaps consisted of two sections, one on the wing itself and the other on the centre section and underside of the fuselage. There was a TAKE-OFF position, in which the outboard slotted flaps lowered 40 degrees and the inboard split flaps 45 degrees, and a LAND position with the outboard flaps at 40 degrees and the inboard flaps at 19 degrees. The lower setting for landing prevented the flap sections on the underside of the fuselage striking arrester wires or contacting the deck during deck landing. However, that proved to be a very rare occurrence, and the use of the LAND position was eventually discontinued. A wing leading-edge droop snoot operated with the flaps and deflected to 19 degrees.

The variable-position speed brakes consisted of two perforated panels under the fuselage centre section forward of the inboard flaps. Like the latter they were in danger of contacting the deck if fully lowered (75 degrees) for landing. They were not very effective in decelerating the aircraft at speeds below 250 knots.

An hydraulic tailskid was interconnected mechanically with the arrester hook and also with the undercarriage. It could also be actuated by throttle movement, being retracted when the throttle was opened fully and lowered when the throttle was retarded to 90% rpm. The actuating control on the arrester hook overrode the other two control switches when the hook was lowered. The arrester hook itself had a double-movement action. It extended mechanically to a horizontal or trail position and then fell vertically. The pilot could retract it hydraulically to the trail position.

On my first flight in F9F-5 Bu.No.125082 on 27th September 1951 I found the cockpit roomy, well laid out, and with a good all-round view. Start-up and taxying were easy, although it took a fair amount of power to get this baby rolling. The take-off was rather unimpressive, and the aircraft gave the feeling of being rather underpowered. Nosewheel lift-off speed was 89 knots, with unstick at 105 knots, and thereafter the Panther accelerated somewhat ponderously to the initial climbing speed of 320 knots. The climb took 7.2 min to 30,000 ft and 14.2 min to 40,000 ft, but only if the maximum tailpipe temperature was allowed to overshoot above 35,000 ft.

Over a series of handling and performance test flights I concluded that the Panther was essentially lacking in the indispensable requirements of a fighter, namely gun-platform stability, manoeuvrability and harmony of control. In brief, it snaked badly with a short-period, small-amplitude oscillation; the stick force per 'g' was too high (8½ lb/'g' at 450 knots at 10,000 ft and 14 lb/'g' at 30,000 ft, both values for mid CG); and the harmony of control was spoilt by the combination of heavy elevators and light ailerons.

Moreover, the lateral control system was poor in that insufficient aileron centering and neutral static lateral control force stability made instrument flying difficult. There was actually provision for artificial spring feel, but the spring was not fitted to the aircraft. The maximum rate of roll was 163 degrees per second at 335 knots, which was slightly below accepted modern fighter standards.

With the hydraulic power boost off there was unpleasant lateral stick play near the neutral stick position, which added to the poor rate of roll and high stick force in that condition made it unsatisfactory for deck landing in the event of a boost failure.

The high-speed characteristics were marred by longitudinal static control force instability, and also a marked loss in elevator effectiveness and undesirable nose-down pitch with speed brake operation. There was also slight buffeting and lateral lurching above M=0.85. The limit safe Mach number of the aircraft was 0.88.

The low-speed characteristics were satisfactory except for a lack of sufficient aerodynamic stall warning, and rather sensitive speed control during a deck landing approach owing to the weakly positive static longitudinal stability, particularly at aft CG. Neither of these defects was serious, and I found it an easy aeroplane to deck-land. View on the approach at 113 knots was very good, but that was a high entry speed for current arrester gear.

At that stage the F9F-5 was fitted with small wing centre section stall fences which were intended to control the spanwise airflow and thus reduce the high landing speed. The fences reduced the stalling speed in the landing configuration by 3½ knots to 98½ knots, but they had no effect on the clean stalling speed of 131 knots. Furthermore, they had an adverse effect on stall warning, so when adopting the stall fences as standard the US Navy also introduced a stall warning stick shaker.

For shipboard operations the wings folded upwards immediately outboard of the air intakes, reducing the overall span to 23 ft 9 in. Catapulting and arresting trials were also carried out at Patuxent River, and the F9F-5 was cleared to be catapulted at gross weights up to 21,500 lb and arrested up to 14,200 lb. I was frequently launched from the H4B pneumatic-hydraulic catapult with various combinations of stores beneath the Panther. The most exciting event in my project calendar, however, was the demonstration of the British BXS-1 steam catapult aboard HMS Perseus, which arrived in US waters in February 1952. I flew F9F-2 Bu.No.123018 (originally an F9F-3) up to the US Navy's Mustin Field, Philadelphia, on the morning of 5th February, then taxied it from the airfield into the adjacent Navy Yard and right alongside Perseus, which was berthed there. The Panther was hoisted aboard by crane, and I made the first launch that afternoon, with the carrier still alongside and a 5 knot tailwind blowing down the catapult.

There were many sceptics around when the captain of Perseus ordered the launch to be made, but he realised that there could be no more impressive a demonstration of the catapult than in such conditions. The acceleration of 4.3 'g' was so smooth that I had difficulty accepting that I had soared away with an endspeed of 126 knots. I landed back at Mustin Field and next day repeated the performance twice, with 8 knot and 6 knot tailwinds. The catapult gave 4.2 'g' and a 127 knot endspeed on the first launch and 4.5 'g' and 132 knots on the second. Perseus put to sea a few days later, and on 12th February I was launched in flat calm sea conditions in Chesapeake Bay with a 7 knot wind. The F9F-2 carried a full fuel load and was shot off at 4.18 'g' with an endspeed of 122 knots, which certainly sped me on my way to Norfolk Naval Air Station.

The F9F-5 had a maximum speed of 526 knots TAS at sea level, a service ceiling of

42,000 ft, and a range of 1,255 nm at 405 knots TAS at 40,000 ft. In Korea, where low-level operations were the order of the day for the US Navy's aircraft carriers, the sea-level turn of speed and the useful endurance were to stand the Panther in good stead. It had limited success in the fighter role but performed creditably as a ground-attack bomber.

In my view, the Panther had been rushed into production and service, and committed to combat over Korea, at too early a stage in its development career, and some of its shortcomings should have been ironed out before it appeared on US Navy carrier decks. It fell rather short of being a great naval fighter, and if it was something of a mediocrity it is perhaps charitable to assume that its indifferent capability was primarily due to pressure under which it was developed by Grumman, combined with the company's inexperience in jet fighter design at the time.

Chapter 25
Grumman J4F Widgeon

Grumman started design work on its G-44 amphibian in August 1939, and the resultant Widgeon made its first flight on 28th June 1940. In all, 51 aircraft were delivered to civil customers and the Portuguese Naval Air Arm. Then the US Coast Guard began taking an interest and Widgeons were built for it under the designation J4F, and subsequently for the US Navy as the J4F-2.

When I first flew the J4F-2 I thought it looked like a smaller and much lighter version of the Grumann G-21 Goose. It carried two crew and three passengers, and

was powered by a pair of 200 hp Ranger L-440 C-5 six-cylinder in-line inverted air-cooled engines driving two-bladed airscrews. It had a span of 40 ft, a length of 31 ft 1 in, a height of 11 ft 5 in, an empty weight of 3,240 lb and a loaded weight of 4,525 lb.

It was an uncomplicated and pleasant aircraft to fly, with good water take-off and alighting characteristics, although it was somewhat underpowered. Its performance was rather mundane, with a rate of climb of 700 ft/min, a top speed of 153 mph at sea level, a crusing speed of 138 mph, a service

The Grumman J4F-1 Widgeon amphibian.

The high length-to-beam-ratio hulled J4F-2 Widgeon.

ceiling of 14,600 ft and a range of 800 miles.

An upgraded civil prototype, the XG-44A, flew in August 1944, and the production of civil Widgeons was resumed before the end of the Second World War. The French Société de Constructions Aéronavales (SCAN) built a few under licence, powered by 220 hp Mathis and Salmson engines.

My flight on the J4F-2 was to prepare me for a flight on a specially modified Widgeon at the US Naval Air Test Center, Patuxent River. This aircraft, Bu. Aer. No.3297, had been modified by the Edo Corporation as a test bed for evaluating low-drag, high length-to-beam-ratio sea-plane hulls. It first flew in May 1948 as a test bed for the half-scale model of the Martin Marlin XP5M-1 hull, which had a length-to-beam-ratio of 8.5:1.

The XJ4F-2 which I flew on 27th September 1951 had a 12.5:1 length-to-beam-ratio hull. It was fitted with a new main undercarriage which, for water operations, swung upwards but remained in the airstream while in flight. The test hull had a pair of windows in its bottom for visual and photographic observation of the water flow at and aft of the step.

The flight tests were concerned with the hydrodynamic rather than the aero-dynamic characteristics, and so were largely confined to water taxying and take-off and landing trials in various sea states in the Chesapeake Bay area.

The view from the cockpit was terrible – I do not recollect ever having so much fuselage nose length ahead of me. In the water it was not easy to taxy because its slim hull had so much keel surface that it was very sensitive to side wind and always had one float digging into the water more than the other, so a lot of ruddering and differential throttling was called for.

The take-off characteristics were generally good, considering that the aircraft was underpowered, but in spite of the sluggish acceleration it got up on to the step rapidly and then unstuck smartly. This was just as well, since the view ahead was virtually nil in that phase of the operation because of the steep angle of the nose combined with seaspray from the propellers. There was very little tendency to porpoise up to sea state 4, but above that the aircraft could dig its nose into the swell and display rather frightening tendencies to emulate a submarine. Take-off had to be aborted immediately in such circumstances.

It was in landing that the experimental hull showed its main benefit. The aircraft's approach attitude was quite flat and the touchdown delightfully smooth, with the hull skimming through the water with a gentle hissing noise rather than the slapping and banging normally associated with flying-boats, including the standard Widgeon. The landing run was longer than for the normal J4F-2, and the control wheel had to be held well back to prevent the nose digging in as speed fell, but this was a small price to pay for the aerodynamic benefits in flight of a beautifully streamlined hull.

Interestingly, this special Widgeon has ended its life on display in the prestigious Smithsonian National Air and Space Museum in Washington DC, so it was obviously assessed as a significant contribution to hydrodynamics.

Chapter 26
Handley Page Halifax VI

Much has been written about the Halifax, which, together with the Avro Lancaster and Short Stirling, formed the backbone of the RAF's wartime Bomber Command. A few details will suffice to refresh memories.

The Halifax was designed to meet Air Ministry Specification B.13/36, and the prototype first flew in October 1939, fitted with four Rolls-Royce Merlin X engines. The production model flew a year later, and the type went into operational service in March 1941. The Marks III, VI, VII, and VIII had Bristol Hercules sleeve-valve radial engines.

The early marks of the Halifax suffered from rudder overbalance, so the fins were increased in area on later marks, and the wing span increased from 98 ft 8 in to 103 ft 8 in as all-up weight increased. The Mk.VI had both of these modifications and was powered by four 1,675 hp Hercules 100 14-cylinder engines. It had seven crew, was armed with two four-gun turrets, one in a dorsal amidships position and the other in the tail, plus a manually-operated gun in the nose, and could carry 14,500 lb of bombs. All the guns were of 0.303 in calibre.

The standard Halifax I.

The Halifax VI.

In night operations over Germany the Halifax had exhibited some undesirable handling characteristics during corkscrew evasive manoeuvres to evade either searchlights or night fighters. Part of the problem was the inadequate lateral control in such situations, and the high wing loading of the aircraft was affecting take-off and landing performance. In an attempt to solve both shortcomings, Halifax VI NP715 was fitted with spoiler-aileron controls similar to those used successfully on the American Northrop Black Widow night fighter, and which had been tested on the latter aircraft at RAE in April 1944. The aim of the spoilers on the Halifax was to enable an increase in the maximum lift coefficent to be gained through added flap area, while giving improved aileron control.

The Halifax system consisted of four closely adjacent scoop spoilers of 20 ft 3 in total span and of an average vertical height of 5.46 in (port) and 6.2 in (starboard), issuing from each wing at a distance well back on the chord behind the transition point. The spoilers decreased in height to allow for decreasing wing thickness from the inboard to outboard locations.

A small tip aileron of 8 ft 11 in span lay behind the two outboard spoilers on each wing and, of course, the spoilers only issued from the wing with the upgoing aileron. Extra flaps had been fitted where the reduced aileron span left free trailing-edge area normally occupied by the long-span ailerons on standard aircraft. The auxiliary flap span on each wing was 12 ft 1 in.

I had previously carried out the Black Widow tests and part of the Halifax corkscrew trials, so I was obviously going to be involved in this project. When I got into the cockpit the first noticeable feature of the layout was the large amount of friction in the aileron control circuit, measured on the ground as 18 lb to move the wheel to starboard and 23 lb to move it to port. Besides this discrepancy in stick force, there was also a discrepancy in the spoiler protrusion height, the starboard mean height being about 1 in higher than the port. This difference was reflected in the aircraft's behaviour in flight, for the rolling performance to starboard was superior to that to port.

The spoiler control response was very good at the normal cruising speed of 200 mph, and improved with increase in speed up to the 260 mph limit of the test. Although the response deteriorated with reduction in speed, it was still fairly good at 140 mph. There was no noticeable lag in response, allowing for the inertia of the wing span. Rate of roll ranged from about 12.5 degrees/sec at 140 mph to 15 degrees/sec at 200 mph and 14 degrees/sec at 260 mph. The forces applied to the control wheel to produce these rates were 40 lb, 50 lb and 70 lb, respectively.

At 140 mph control response and rate of roll were considerably adversely affected with the lowering of the standard flaps, but this loss of lateral performance was almost completely regained with further lowering of the auxiliary flaps.

A series of stalls was carried out, both to check lateral control at very low speeds and to determine if there was any real gain in maximum lift coefficient from the system. The all-up stall occurred at 112 mph and at 95 mph with standard flaps down. Lowering of the auxiliary flaps gave a strong nose-down change of trim and further reduced the stalling speed to 91 mph. The stall warning was a slight buffet, heavying up just before the nose dropped away evenly. All of the stalls displayed similar characteristics, except that the buffeting was milder in the all-up condition. In each case the use of aileron would not pick up a wing at the stall, and if the engines were opened up evenly to aid recovery after the stall the aircraft would roll quite violently.

In normal flight, turns on aileron only were well-nigh perfect, but on rudder only a slight skid occurred. Very little yaw was induced by the protruding spoiler, and there was no noticeable difference in control characteristics caused by rapid control wheel application as opposed to normal. Self-centering of the ailerons was positive, except at low speeds.

At this stage it should be remarked that the standard Halifax was not an easy aeroplane to land. Forward view from the cockpit was impeded by large windscreen struts, the throttles were difficult to manipulate, and the trimmer controls were badly scattered in layout. The drag of the large undercarriage was such that, on lowering it, considerable power was required to maintain height or reduce the rate of descent. The approach attitude was steep, requiring a good backward pull for hold-off, and this was aggravated further by the large nose-down change of trim when the throttles were closed. The Lancaster by comparison was a dolly to land.

The case for the spoilers was obviously going to depend largely on the advantages offered by the system in landing. In the circuit at 135 mph lateral control was reasonably good, but at 115 mph with standard flaps lowered it was terrible. However, lowering the auxiliary flaps improved this state of affairs to acceptable proportions at 110 mph, but I found I was out of backward elevator trim at this approach speed and could not effect a three-point landing because of the high elevator stick force required to change attitude on cutting the engines and holding off.

The case for a baulked landing was also very shaky, and the engines had to be opened up slowly and with the starboard throttles leading to prevent the aircraft rolling smartly to starboard.

The conclusion, therefore, was that the spoiler-aileron control system was very similar in effect to the lateral control on a standard Halifax, except that it fell down at low speeds. There was a definite gain in maximum lift coefficient, but this was offset by the trim troubles on landing introduced by the added auxiliary flap. This was not a very successful experiment, and showed that an effective system integrally designed into one aircraft cannot necessarily be transplanted into a very different type of aircraft with the same degree of success.

Chapter 27
Hawker Fury

When I first beheld the Hawker Fury, it was one of the most exciting aeroplanes I had ever seen. Perhaps the occasion lent enchantment to the view, for I was a schoolboy spectator at an air pageant, where a squadron of Furies were thrilling the crowd with their flying and aerobatics. My love of flying had already been sparked off before this spectacle, but it was now fanned into a consuming conflagration. Some years were to pass before I achieved my ambition to fly the Fury, but it was worth every moment of the long wait.

There was no real prototype of the Fury, which evolved from Air Ministry Specification F.20/27 for a high-performance interceptor. The Hawker answer to this challenge took advantage of the company's newly developed techniques of metal construction with excellent strength-to-weight ratios, and the resulting Hawker biplane was a single-seat design which the Air Ministry insisted should be powered by a Bristol Mercury radial engine. With an uncowled Mercury VI eventually installed in 1930 it achieved 202 mph at 10,000 ft.

Sydney Camm, Hawker's chief designer, was convinced that the in-line engine offered far greater potential for such a fighter, and persuaded his company to embark on a private venture development of the F.20/27. This aeroplane was powered by a 420 hp Rolls-Royce F.XIA, and later by a 480 hp F.XIS which gave it a speed of 205 mph at 13,000 ft. The Hornet, as this aircraft was named, aroused the interest of the Air Ministry to such a degree that Specification F.13/30 was written around it, and an initial production order was placed for 21 machines. The production model was altered to become the Fury, fitted with a fully supercharged Rolls-Royce Kestrel Mk.IIS 12-cylinder Vee in-line liquid-cooled engine of 525 hp.

In its initial production form the Fury was virtually identical with the Hornet prototype, being an unequal-span biplane with staggered wings, of mixed metal and wood construction. Its first flight took place at Brooklands on 25th March 1931. With a top wing span of 30 ft and a length of 26 ft 8 in it was a small aeroplane. Its empty weight was 2,623 lb and the loaded weight was 3,490 lb.

The top and bottom wings had the same aerofoil section but were unequal in all other respects, the lower wings having less chord, less span (26 ft 0¼ in) more dihedral and more incidence than the upper wings. Frise-type ailerons were fitted to the upper mainplane only. The wings and fuselage were fabric covered, except that the engine and front portion of the fuselage were covered by aluminium panels. The fin was offset 3 degrees to port to counteract propeller slipstream effect. The V-type cross-axle undercarriage had oleo-rubber shock absorbers, and the swivelling tailskid had a rubber-in-compression shock absorber.

By the time I got around to flying a Fury it had been upgraded to the Mk.II, with a more powerful Kestrel VI engine of 640 hp driving a fixed-pitch two-bladed Watts wooden propeller. This was the same propeller as for the Fury I, and its 9 ft 2 in diameter gave a ground clearance of only 4 in with the tail raised. The engine radiator was mounted below the fuselage between the undercarriage V struts. Fuel was carried in two tanks in the forward fuselage of the Fury I, with a total capacity of 50

The Hawker Fury, an aerobatic gem.

Imperial gallons, but the Fury II had an extra fuselage tank forward of the cockpit, giving a total capacity of 65 Imperial gallons. These changes increased the Fury II's empty weight to 2,734 lb and its loaded weight to 3,700 lb.

The armament of the Fury comprised 2×0.303-in Vickers machine-guns mounted on the upper front fuselage and synchronised to fire through the airscrew disc. Each gun had 600 rounds of ammunition. Such light firepower really required the attacking pilot to close in very near the target to ensure a kill.

The cockpit, which was entered by means of two hand/toe apertures on the port side, was positioned about halfway along the fuselage and just aft of the trailing edge of the upper wing. The humped lines of the upper fuselage raised the cockpit enough to give the pilot a very good view for a biplane layout. Instrumentation was basically functional, and no radio was fitted in the earlier models.

Starting was accomplished by literally winding up the engine using a Hucks starter with its shaft mating in a dog on the propeller boss. The Kestrel had a lovely throaty roar like a supercharged racing car which seemed particularly appropriate to the Fury. The view for taxying was poor ahead, so the aircraft had to be swung from side to side, but this was easy with the efficient hydraulic toe-brakes. Take-off required a fair amount of right rudder and was bouncy on grass but short in length of run. The initial rate of climb at 140 mph was over 2,000 ft/min, which was superb for the 1930s.

In cruising flight at 160 mph the controls were all light and effective, the harmony of control being particularly splendid, with the elevators just a bit heavier than the other two controls. Stability was positive both longitudinally and directionally, but neutral laterally. Rate of roll seemed to me to be inferior to that of the Gloster Gauntlet, which I had already flown. Indeed, the Fury felt less nippy than the Gloster fighter. Certainly the Gauntlet's successor, the Gladiator, outstripped the Fury in almost every respect. However, I am really splitting hairs when it comes to general handling qualities, for all three were superb aerobatic aeroplanes just screaming to be thrown around the skies.

The stall in the Fury was denoted by a gentle nose drop at 63 mph, and the spin was equally innocuous, with recovery possible in half a turn. This was the sort of machine to generate great confidence in both the tyro and the experienced fighter pilot.

Landing the Fury was straightforward, for the view ahead was just acceptable in the glide, and anyway it was an easy aeroplane to sideslip, either to enhance the view or lose excess height. At 70 mph all of the controls were still effective right down to touchdown.

The Fury Mk. I had a maximum speed of 207 mph at 14,000 ft, a service ceiling of 28,000 ft and a range of 305 miles. The Mk.II had a top speed of 223 mph, could climb to 10,000 ft in 3 min 50 secs, had a service ceiling of 29,500 ft and a range of 270 miles.

In 1933 Hawker embarked on a private venture High Speed Fury to investigate ways of increasing speed by the use of more powerful engines and modified wing planforms. Modified upper and lower wings were fitted, as were V-type interplane struts instead of the standard N-type. This aircraft was acquired by Rolls-Royce in July 1935, and in August 1936 was fitted with a Kestrel XVI which gave it a top speed of 231.5 mph at 14,800 ft.

The Hawker Fury was the first RAF fighter to have a speed of over 200 mph in level flight. It certainly impressed foreign air forces and was sold in various custom-built forms to at least five different countries, bringing valuable business to the parent company. It was, however, its aerobatic prowess rather than its speed which built such a great reputation for the Fury and made it so beloved of the British public.

It was a very popular aeroplane with pilots and served in RAF squadrons until 1939, but saw only limited action with the air forces of Spain, Yugoslavia and South Africa. Certainly it belonged to the golden era of biplane fighters, and there is no doubt that it sowed in Sydney Camm's mind the design seeds of his wonderchild, the Hawker Hurricane, to which Britain largely owed its survival in the early years of the Second World War. For my own part, I remember the Fury as a thing of beauty that simply oozed élan, and that must have been the spirit in which it was always flown.

Chapter 28
Hawker Typhoon

Like the Bristol Beaufighter, the Hawker Typhoon design concept preceded the relevant Air Ministry Specification, which in the latter's case was F.18/37 for a single-seat fighter powered by one of the new 24-cylinder engines being developed by both Rolls-Royce and Napier, and armed with 12×0.303 machine-guns.

Since the future of the Rolls-Royce Vulture and Napier Sabre was somewhat unpredictable, the Hawker Aircraft Company decided on a belt and braces policy and designed an airframe with two different engine installations. In the event the Vulture-engined Tornado prototype was the first to fly, on 6th October 1939, although the teething troubles of the Vulture, combined with the priority on Rolls-Royce Merlin production, led to that engine being abandoned.

The Sabre-engined Typhoon first flew on 24th February 1940, and during its early testing a serious fault almost led to the loss of the prototype. The forward half of the fuselage, extending just aft of the cockpit, was a braced tubular structure similar to that on the Hurricane, but aft of this the

The brutish Hawker Typhoon IA.

fuselage consisted of a monocoque shell attached at four points to the fore structure, and there it was that failure occurred. Tail weakness was to continue to plague the Typhoon and cast a shadow over its reputation.

The first prototype was armed with the 12 Browning guns called for in the Specification and was designated the Mk.IA, whereas the second prototype had 4×20 mm Hispano cannon and became the Mk.IB. The Typhoon's appearance exemplified brute force.

It soon became evident that the Typhoon had a considerable number of short-comings in both reliability and perform-ance, as well as in pilot safety features. A spate of accidents occurred, caused by the whole tail unit detaching in flight owing to fatigue failure at the rear fuselage transport joint, and these were compounded by failures of the Sabre engine.

As an interceptor fighter the Typhoon had a disappointing rate of climb and a poor service ceiling. The cockpit suffered from carbon monoxide contamination by engine fumes, the hood fairing gave poor rearward view in combat, and in early models a car-door type of pilot access made escape by parachute difficult.

I first became involved with the Typhoon in tests to gauge the effectiveness of the rear fuselage strengthening modifications, and these tests were also in preparation for a series of dives to investigate the aircraft's Mach number limits due to compressibility effects. It has to be remembered that these were the early days of transonic flight, and we were just feeling our way towards what some then believed was the impregnable 'sound barrier'.

My first flight on the type was in a Mk.IB to measure level speed performance at +6 lb boost, 3,500 rpm, which was the maximum one-hour rating. During these runs I experienced about half-a-dozen sudden engine cuts, which were complete yet momentary, but the resultant yaw each time was vicious and obviously put immense strain on the tail. These hiccups

were a feature of the 2,100 hp Sabre I driving a three-bladed de Havilland propeller. They were one of the reasons for the series of reduced power limitations put on the Sabre by the Air Ministry in the early 1940s, and these in turn caused reductions in performance. Indeed, the Typhoon was going through such a bad patch that officialdom gave serious thought to withdrawing the aircraft from service.

In the Second World War the Machmeter had not yet been introduced into operational fighters, and indeed up to 1942 the Pilot's Notes gave only a limiting diving speed based on structural considerations. Starting with the Spitfire IX, a table of limiting indicated airspeeds against height bands was given, to take account of compressibility effects which could cause loss of control if these limits were exceeded. Such a table was already in existence for the Typhoon, and read as follows:

Altitude	20,000 ft	25,000 ft	30,000 ft	35,000 ft
IAS	425 mph	385 mph	340 mph	—

The absence of a limiting speed at 35,000 ft was an indication of the Typhoon's high-altitude shortcomings, as such a speed was given at this altitude for all contemporary Allied fighters.

The speeds given in the Typhoon's table were, after allowing for position error, equivalent to a Mach number of 0.79, which was higher than for any contemporary piston-engined fighter except the Spitfire IX. Our job at RAE Farnborough was to determine how critical this limiting Mach number was if taken to the ultimate loss of control. These tests were normally started at the highest possible altitude, so that if loss of control did occur in the dive the Mach number would automatically reduce as height was lost, provided the dive angle was kept constant, and thus allow control to be regained.

The aircraft to be used for the compressibility dive tests was Typhoon IB EK154, fitted with a Machmeter and powered by a 2,200 hp Sabre IIA. The aircraft was climbed to 32,000 ft and after a

3 min level run at full throttle at that height was half rolled and the nose allowed to drop 30 degrees before half rolling again to maintain that dive angle. The indicated Mach number (IMN) had built up to 0.82 by 27,000 ft, with moderate buffeting, then at 0.83 a noticeable nose-down change of trim occurred and at the same time the buffeting increased. Finally, at IMN=0.84, the nose-down trim change increased dramatically and even a two-handed pull on the stick could not effect recovery. I could just manage to keep the dive from steepening, and held on with considerable effort until, at 20,000 ft, the nose began slowly to rise; by 18,000 ft recovery was complete. From these tests it was clear that the true limiting Mach number of the Typhoon was 0.79 and the true critical Mach number was 0.81.

The hard truth was that the Typhoon was a good performer at low altitudes but a poor fighter above 10,000 ft. It had earlier become obvious that the Typhoon had great potential as a ground-attack aircraft, and so it proved. It was the task of the Aeroplane and Armament Experimental Establishment at Boscombe Down to check out the carriage of weapons at high indicated airspeeds at low level, but if some unacceptable feature displayed itself, then it could be referred to the RAE for further investigation.

Such a problem was posed by the 1,000 lb incendiary bomb, which displayed unacceptable buffeting characteristics and had to have an elongated centre section added by Farnborough scientists. The unmodified bombs were slung one under each wing section between the cannon, protruding well ahead of the leading edge and slightly behind the trailing edge, and I made a flight with these in Typhoon IB MN519 on 30th November 1944. Four dives were made at 2,800 rpm with one-third throttle opening and radiator closed, and revealed serious wing buffeting which made the whole trailing edge of the mainplanes vibrate perceptibly. At 390 mph the buffeting was sufficient to cause the external cockpit step to release itself in spasmodic jerks against the action of its spring-loaded mechanism. The buffet became so acute at 410 mph at 4,000 ft that the test was terminated.

On 14th January 1945 these tests were repeated in Typhoon IB MN943, but with the modified bombs. The same low-frequency vibrations started at speeds from 180 mph, and seemed to run from the top engine cowling along the fuselage in the climb and in level flight. In the dives the vibration gave way to buffeting at 380 mph and increased in severity until at 420 mph it became acute and was accompanied by a fairly violent tendency to roll to the left. However, there was no visible movement in the wing skin and no tail buffet. This was obviously a case of 'back to the drawing board'.

Fortunately not all underwing weapons carried by the Typhoon gave such trouble, and it was a particularly deadly ground-attack aircraft when fitted with eight 3 in rocket projectiles with 60 lb heads. Indeed, for an aircraft that at one stage in its life had been threatened with extinction it had a fine battle record during the Normandy invasion, and all-in-all 3,330 of the type were built. The Typhoon could be said to have succeeded in spite of itself, and the final production version of the IB, with the 2,260 hp Sabre IIC, a four-bladed propeller, faired cannon, and a tear-drop hood seemed to give the old warrior a new look of confidence.

Chapter 29
Hawker Tempest V

After the shaky start of the Typhoon it must have seemed improbable that there would be a Typhoon II, but this in fact was the designation of the design tendered by the Hawker company to meet Air Ministry Specification F.10/41, and which eventually became the Tempest.

Like the Typhoon, the basic design of the Tempest catered for alternative power-plants, and in this case three different engines were considered – the Napier Sabre, the Bristol Centaurus radial, and the Rolls-Royce Griffon. The first prototype to fly, on 2nd September 1942, was the Tempest V powered by a Sabre IIA of 2,180 hp.

The Tempest was distinguishable from the Typhoon by its elliptical, thin-section wing, which necessitated the reduction of the amount of fuel carried in the wings. Consequently an extra fuel bay was inserted in the fuselage behind the engine, and this lengthening of the fuselage forward called for increased fin area aft. The end result was a sleek, powerful looking aeroplane of considerable aesthetic beauty.

The first production Tempest V flew on 21st June 1943, and the first machines entered operational service in April 1944.

The elegant and splendid Tempest V.

The more elegant and still splendid Centaurus-engined Tempest II.

This turned out to be most timely, because the German V.1 flying-bomb offensive was launched in June 1944. The V.1 could attain a normal operational speed of 400 mph at heights usually between 1,000 and 2,500 ft. This severely taxed the interception capabilities of British fighters, and some bombs were getting through to London and beyond. I can vouch for this as my first home in Aldershot was completely demolished when a V.1 impacted in the garden, seriously injuring our charlady, injuring my wife and killing our dog.

About mid-June a crash programme was initiated to improve the low-level performance of the Spitfire, Tempest V, and Mustang III by using a specially developed 150 octane aromatic fuel to give abnormally high power for strictly short bursts. The engine attrition rate would of course be high, but the urgency of the situation demanded drastic measures.

I was very involved in these exhilarating trials requiring high speed runs at ground level, during which the Spitfire XIV with its Griffon boosted to +19 lb reached 365 mph, the Tempest V with its Sabre boosted to +10¼ lb hit 405 mph, and the Mustang III with its Merlin boosted to +25 lb actually attained 420 mph.

During these trials I was flying Tempest V JN735 on 26th July at just after 7 o'clock in the evening, and had completed a 5 min level run at 1,000 ft at +9 lb boost, 3,650 rpm, which was the maximum obtainable with the airscrew pitch lever fully forward. I then climbed through cloud to 6,000 ft, where the second run was made under similar conditions, for it was known that the V.1 could fly up to almost 10,000 ft.

The third run was made at 7,000 ft, at which height only +8½ lb boost was obtainable at full throttle, and after 3½ min I detected a slight smell of burning coming from the floor of the cockpit. A quick check of the engine instruments showed zero oil pressure and oil temperature, with the coolant temperature 108°C. Since the engine had never faltered I suspected oil gauge failures, but throttled back to –4 lb boost and 2,900 rpm and asked for an emergency homing on the R/T, which I was given. I flew on this course at the same height and low engine settings as before until I thought I was near base, when I decided to descend through the solid cloud (top 5,800 ft and base 2,300 ft). On entering the darkness of the cloud I could see the whole top engine cowling glowing hot between the two sets of exhausts, although this had been unapparent to me in the bright sunshine. However, the engine was still running, so I continued the descent, but before I broke cloud the engine began to misfire badly and the propeller started to overspeed. I immediately pulled the constant-speed lever back to the fully coarse stop, but the revs. reached 4,200 and then there was a loud bang in the engine, followed by a spray of oil which covered the windscreen.

In order to see out I had to undo my safety harness and peer round the opaque windscreen. The propeller had seized solid, and the fire under the cowling had now burst out into intense white flames which were also creeping into the cockpit through the floor near the rudder pedals, so the underside must have been well alight too, a fact which was later confirmed by ground witnesses. The heat round my feet hastened my decision to abandon the aircraft.

I removed my helmet and trimmed the aircraft for level flight at 1,600 ft and 170 mph, then stood up on the seat and put my left leg over the port side of the cockpit before reaching inside to pull the stick hard over towards me, so that when the aircraft reached an angle of bank of about 60 degrees I could kick myself free. The altimeter had read 1,200 ft when I glanced at it as I grabbed the control column spadegrip.

When I pulled the parachute ripcord I could see I was heading for open fields, but I was hardly ready for the touchdown because I was watching the Tempest, which hit the ground and exploded some 200 yards from a small pond into which I found myself deposited. From this point the drama gave way to sheer comedy.

The pond that received my unexpected visit was shallow and not particularly salubrious, so I moved as smartly as I could to its edge, only to find myself face to face with the only other occupant of the field – a very large unfriendly looking black bull. As I moved a few steps nearer it lowered its head and snorted through its ringed nose. Discretion being the better part of valour, I did a smart about turn and headed for the opposite side of the pond, but I had just got there when I realised that I had been beaten to it by my bovine acquaintance, who was determined to provide a personal reception service. There was nothing for it but to await deliverance in some form or another.

Alerted by the exploding aircraft, the local fire brigade and police soon arrived, but baulked at the sight of the bull. There was then a hiatus while the police found the owner, who appeared with a short rope which he passed through the animal's nose ring and then gently led him off like a poodle. I may be wrong, but I could swear that the bull winked at me as he departed.

Although Britain's first operational jet fighter, the Gloster Meteor I, was pressed into service to combat the 'doodlebug menace', it was outflown at low level by the Tempest V, which accounted for 638 flying bombs out of the RAF's total score of 1,771 destroyed during the period 13th June to 5th September 1944.

Our other great interest in the Tempest V at the RAE was in its high Mach number characteristics, and these proved to be very similar to those of the Typhoon, except that it had a limiting Mach number of 0.81 true and a critical Mach number of 0.83 true. At the latter speed the nose-down trim change was very strong, and a full-blooded pull was required to keep the dive angle constant until the altitude had fallen to about 15,000 ft, when recovery could be effected.

In our transonic research at the RAE we often exceeded the so-called critical Mach number, which was the limit advised to the Services as being that beyond which there was a grave risk of loss of control of the aircraft. In our case this was not a foolhardy venture, but a controlled step-by-step investigation into a region of risk, each step being analysed from the records obtained from special instruments carried in the aircraft. We were of course in a war situation and could not afford to take an excessive amount of time, so some of the steps were larger than would be made in peacetime, and this could increase the risk element.

On 5th September 1944 I was carrying out a series of tests for the Aerodynamics Department in a Tempest V to measure the effect of drag at high speed by diving the aircraft through a timed altitude range of 2,000 ft, commencing at 7,000 ft and descending to 5,000 ft at steady speeds ranging from 390 mph to 525 mph indicated airspeed (IAS).

The last dive was started at 25,000 ft from a full-throttle level run, then bunting into a fairly shallow dive to 22,000 ft where MS gear was engaged, the throttle set full open, the airscrew pitch adjusted to fully fine to give 3,700 rpm, the elevator trimmed nose-down, and the rudder trimmed to starboard in a position gauged from the previous dive to 470 mph.

At 12,000 ft I experienced slight buffeting at 515 mph IAS, and at 11,000 ft found myself rapidly overshooting the desired IAS of 525 mph. I began to ease back on the stick, but it was frozen solid, and even a strong two-handed pull had no effect. In fact I had a runaway situation on my hands, and the IAS kept on building up to a peak of 560 mph IAS at 9,000 ft, and maintained this speed to 5,000 ft. During this peak period the boost had reached +9 lb/sq.in, but I dared not remove either of my hands from the stick to touch the throttle as the starboard wing was now drooping, presumably because the aircraft was out of trim on the rudder, and I had to make a really tough physical effort to keep the stick central laterally whilst maintaining maximum backward pressure all the time. It is truly surprising the strength you find when survival is at stake. To add to the critical atmosphere, the buffeting had become acute and seemed especially bad forward of the cockpit.

On passing through 5,000 ft the elevator started to bite and I could feel the nose rising almost imperceptibly at first, then more positively until it passed through the level flight position at about 1,500 ft. I have to admit to a feeling of considerable relief.

Examination of the aircraft after landing showed signs of strain in the region of the engine cowling. As this Tempest was fitted with a leading-edge pitot, the Aerodynamics Department calculated the true Mach number attained to be 0.87, which was the highest ever recorded on a Tempest. We certainly had not intended to go that far, but the best laid plans of mice and men . . .

The Tempest V was a great aircraft to fly, having the main assets of a fighter with excellent harmony of control, a good rate of roll, and being stable directionally and laterally but slightly unstable longitudinally. However, it had a very sharp stall without any warning whatsoever, and it was deficient in high-altitude performance. For landing, the aileron control was sluggish, as was the elevator control once the flaps and undercarriage were lowered, and the trim speed in the powered approach configuration was too high. Not a perfect aeroplane perhaps, but certainly a very good one indeed.

Chapter 30
Heinkel He 64

On 11 November 1932 a number of RAE test pilots were invited by Messrs Handley Page Ltd to fly the Heinkel He 64 from their airfield at Radlett. This sporting aeroplane had been designed by Dr Heinkel to participate in the third International European Circuit, held in the summer of 1932, and to exploit his latest thoughts on aerodynamic streamlining.

The He 64 was a low-wing monoplane of wooden construction with an unusually slender well-faired fuselage of oval cross-section, and a long cockpit with two seats in tandem covered by a streamlined Perspex canopy. The plywood wing was slotted to a new Heinkel design, and underneath the centre section were the main legs of the braced non-retractable undercarriage. The span was 32 ft 8 in, the length 27 ft, the height 6 ft 6 in, the empty weight 937 lb and loaded weight 1,628 lb. It was powered by a 150 hp Argus As8R 6-cylinder in-line air-cooled engine driving a two-bladed fixed-pitch wooden propeller, with the engine cowling smoothly faired into the fuselage.

The European Circuit covered 4,700 miles, staging from Berlin via Warsaw, Prague and Vienna to Rome, and thence to

The pencil-like and somewhat eccentric Heinkel He 64.

Florence, Nice, Lyons, Stuttgart, Bonn and Paris. The third stage was to Amsterdam, Copenhagen, Gothenburg, Hamburg and, finally, Berlin. Six days were normally allowed to complete the Circuit, but the German pilot, Hans Seidemann, in the He 64 took only half that time and created a sensation in world aviation circles.

The performance figures given by the Germans for this pencil-like aeroplane gave a top speed of 152 mph and a cruising speed of 140 mph. Initial rate of climb was 885 ft/min, and the service ceiling was 17,750 ft. Range varied from 560 miles to 930 miles, depending on the cruising speed used.

The combined report of the RAE test pilots makes interesting reading, as all commented that the He 64 demonstrated unusual flying characteristics. Some difficulty was experienced in taxying because of the long fuselage and non-tracking tailskid, together with the tendency of the tail to rise if the brakes were used. The wide-track undercarriage felt rather harsh.

Take-off was effected by holding the control column fully back from the moment the throttle was opened. Unstick followed a short run of 410 ft, and the aircraft could then be climbed at an angle of some 40 degrees. Full control around all three axes was available throughout the take-off and steep climb.

In cruising flight the elevators and rudder were light and effective, while the ailerons were very positive in effect but fairly heavy, largely due to friction in the control circuit, and they had a tendency to snatch.

There was a most noticeable difference in the performance with and without the slats and inner flaps in operation. Owing presumably to the effect of the slipstream, the inner slats did not operate simultaneously, but Heinkel intended to overcome this by connecting the two with a torque tube. The inner slats opened at a lower speed than the outer ones.

The aircraft could not be stalled in the normal manner. A bad whip stall was, however, induced by flying engine-on with the fuselage at an angle of about 30 degrees to the horizontal, then closing the throttle and quickly opening it and closing it again, whereupon the left wing and nose dropped very suddenly indeed, although control was soon regained.

Glide landings were made with the slats open, and this gave a surprisingly nose-high attitude. The angle of the flight path was very steep and the vertical velocity somewhat high, so a quick opening of the throttle had to be made to reduce the rate of descent and enable quick depression of the nose for a three-point landing. Unless that was done, the aircraft would strike the ground with excessive vertical velocity. The forward view on the glide was bad because of the nose-high attitude, and it was necessary to yaw the aircraft from side to side to see ahead.

Normal landings at lower angles of incidence could be effected, but under such conditions a long float was likely to occur owing to the clean design of the aircraft. Moreover, the increase of lift when the slats opened was most marked and disconcerting under those conditions.

Although the He 64 was a sportplane, aerobatics were not permitted. The consensus of opinion of the RAE test pilots was that it was generally a pleasant aircraft to fly, but it possessed characteristics necessitating the development of a new technique for taking-off and landing.

Chapter 31
Henschel Hs 129B

The Hs 129 began life as a problem child with inherent design problems. It was designed in 1937, completed in 1938 and flown in the spring of 1939 as the answer to a German Air Ministry specification for a small twin-engined ground-attack aircraft. The concept of the Henschel design team was that the core of the aircraft should be a cockpit box of 6 to 12 mm armour plates spot-welded together, with the windscreen of 75 mm armoured glass, and the two Argus As 10 engines should be protected by 5 mm armoured plate. The result was an underpowered aeroplane with a cramped cockpit and appalling view, and poor handling characteristics. Inevitably the Luftwaffe refused to accept it, but a redesign would have involved such a huge delay that early in 1941 the Air Ministry ordered Henschel to produce a modified version powered by captured Gnome-Rhône 14M 4/5 radial engines.

The modified Hs 129Bs appeared in 1942, and a number were used for experiments with the carriage of a large variety of weapons. The standard B-1 had an armament of 2×20 mm MG FF cannon and 2×7.9

The ponderous Henschel Hs 129B tank buster.

mm MG 17 machine-guns. However, the weapons experiments resulted in a new production series, the Hs 129B-2, which was purely a gun-carrier, and this was the type that the RAE foraging team found at Gilze-Rizen airfield in Holland, whither I was despatched to fly it on 10th September 1945.

On examination this aircraft turned out to be an Hs 129B-2/R2 (Werknummer 141687) fitted with a 30 mm MK 103 cannon in an underfuselage mounting as well as 2×20 mm MG 151/20 cannon and 2×7.9 MG 17 machine-guns.

The Hs 129B was a low-wing monoplane of all-metal construction with a remarkable amount of nose armour, which weighed 2,370 lb. With a span of 44 ft 6 in, a length of 33 ft 3 in and a height of 10 ft 8 in it was a small, single-seat twin specially designed to attack enemy tanks. Power was provided by two 700 hp Gnome-Rhône 14M 4/5 14-cylinder radial air-cooled engines driving three-bladed Ratier electrically-operated constant-speed airscrews. There were two self-sealing wing fuel tanks, each of 45 Imperial gallons, and one in the fuselage with a capacity of 44 Imperial gallons. The empty weight was 8,940 lb and the loaded weight was 11,250 lb.

The control system was conventional, with the entire trailing edge of the wing hinged, the outer sections acting as slotted ailerons and the inner sections as slotted flaps. The rudder and elevators were slightly horn balanced, with electrically operated trim tabs, and the tailplane incidence was adjustable on the ground.

The cockpit of the Hs 129B was very cramped, to such a degree that some of the engine instruments were mounted externally on the inner side of the engine cowlings. The view ahead was very poor, largely due to the thickness and standard of the armoured windshield, which in rain was virtually opaque. Start-up of the Gnome-Rhônes was by inertia starter, but there was something about their running sound that did not inspire confidence, and in fact I learned later that they had proved very unreliable in service, although they gave no trouble on my flight.

In flight, the Hs 129B was a lumbering aeroplane with very poor manoeuvrability due to the high stick forces and very positive stability around all three axes. The stick force/'g' was so excessive that the aircraft really had to be flown on the trim tabs, which fortunately were quite high geared.

The performance was rather abysmal, with a rate of climb just over 1,000 ft/min and a top speed of 255 mph at 22,000 ft if you could be bothered to clamber your way up to what was a dizzy height for the Hs 129B. I shudder to think what the Hs 129A must have been like with its 465 hp engines, narrower cockpit and handwheel operated trim tabs. I spoke to one Luftwaffe pilot who flew the A model, and he called it 'ein Ungeheuer' – a monster.

The Hs 129B was used by the Luftwaffe as a test bed for an astonishing range of weapons including the 37 mm BK 3.7 and the 50 mm BK 5 cannon, 4 kg SD 4 bombs with hollow-charge warheads, the mighty 75 mm BK 7.5 gun which had a barrel recoil distance of almost 3 ft, and the Gero flame thrower. The most interesting weapon, however, was the SG 113A rocket mortar, which consisted of six single-barrelled mortars in a rhomboid-shaped mounting firing 77 mm shells vertically downwards and triggered by a photo-electric cell.

The Hs 129B was a terrible aeroplane from a pilot's point of view, but was a successful tank buster, although its loss rate of 1 in 5 was unacceptably, but not surprisingly high.

Chapter 32
Lavochkin La-7

There was a short spell immediately after the Second World War when Allied tests pilots like myself could enter the Russian zone of occupation and be heartily welcomed, particularly if you were British. Britain's record of sending aircraft and pilots to Russia in its hour of need gave us a special status in the eyes of the Russians, and this benevolence could even be stretched to being allowed to fly the odd aircraft with the red star on the fuselage. So it was that I came to fly the La-7, and a very interesting experience it turned out to be.

I had flown the Il-2 Stormovik assault bomber on the previous day in June 1945, and had not been very impressed. This type was in abundance everywhere, and was the obvious trade-in offer for a flight in my Fairey Firefly, but I managed to convey to the one Russian with any authority, and who could speak German, that I felt I had been short-changed and that I expected

something more akin to the Firefly in performance. So after some more horse trading a deal was struck that, in exchange for another flight in my mount, I could have a go at an La-7.

I was quite impressed with the look of the La-7, which had good aerodynamic lines except for its somewhat bulbous nose, but this proboscis at least gave a hint of plenty of engine power being available.

This low-wing monoplane single-seat fighter was generally of wooden construction with stressed plywood skinning. The wings, which unlike the La-5 had metal spars, carried outer-wing automatic leading-edge slats, fabric covered ailerons with fixed trim tabs on their trailing edges, and split flaps of duralumin sheet. The horn-balanced rudder and the elevators were fabric covered and had trim tabs. The wide-track undercarriage retracted inwards to lie flat in the wings, and the tailwheel was

The Russian La-7 hot-rod fighter.

also hydraulically retractable. With a span of 32 ft 2 in, a length of 28 ft 2 in, and a height of 8 ft 4 in it was a comparatively small aeroplane.

The powerplant was a 2,000 hp Shvetsov M-82FN 14-cylinder radial air-cooled engine with a two-stage supercharger and direct fuel injection, driving a VISh105V three-bladed controllable-pitch metal propeller. The total fuel capacity was 134 Imperial gallons distributed between three tanks. The armament was 2×20 mm Shpital'ny Vladimirov cannon synchronised to fire through the propeller disc, with 200 rounds of ammunition per gun. The empty weight was 6,200 lb, and the loaded weight 7,480 lb. I believe a third cannon was fitted to some La-7s, but I saw no sign of such an addition on my aircraft.

The cockpit was entered using a retractable step on the port side and then stepping on to the wing root. Once settled, I realised how snug the cockpit was and, like the Stormovik, how rudimentary the instruments were for blind flying. The aircraft had a smell of birch and resin mixed with that distinctive smell of all Russian aircraft. There was an armoured glass windshield and an armourglass panel behind the pilot's head, but I couldn't see any sign of armour plating for the pilot's protection.

The compressed air start-up was made with the assistance of a Russian pilot leaning into the cockpit, and it certainly seemed a little complicated, but the engine burst into life with a healthy roar. The view for taxying was not good ahead, but the pneumatic brakes were effective and easily controllable from the control column brake lever, so that the aircraft could be swung from side to side.

The take-off was made with neutral elevator trim and full right rudder trim, and the engine front cooling louvres open, while the side cooling louvres which had been open for taxying were now shut. Full power and 2,500 rpm was used, and gave excellent acceleration and a strong left swing which could be held on rudder.

Unstick occurred at 200 km/h (124 mph). Once the wheels had been raised, the undercarriage control lever had to be returned to neutral, and power reduced to 0.9 atas (13.2 lb boost) and revs. to 2,300. At an airspeed of 260 km/h (161 mph) the rate of climb was impressive, being of the order of 4,000 ft/min, but I discontinued the climb at about 20,000 ft because I had some difficulty getting the right combination of cooling-louvre settings to keep the cylinder head temperatures within limits. However, I had enough time to check stability on the way up, and found it to be neutral both longitudinally and laterally, but positive directionally.

Levelling off into the cruise at 0.6 atas (8.8 lb boost) and 2,000 rpm, which gave an estimated true airspeed of 302 mph, I threw the aeroplane around and found the harmony of control quite delightful and indeed as good as that of any contemporary piston-engined fighter I had flown. Stability was still neutral about the longitudinal and lateral axes and positive directionally. The ailerons were particularly light and effective, and gave a high rate of roll, while the elevators were moderately light and produced a good rate of turn, whose manoeuvre limit was enhanced when the slats opened at about 300 km/h (185 mph) until finally the 'g' stall occurred at 200 km/h (125 mph), when the wings started to rock and the nose fell away into a steep dive. Aerobatics were easy and a delight to perform, and the spinning characteristics displayed a steep, fast rate of rotation with quick response to use of normal recovery procedure.

Stalls at 10,000 ft exhibited remarkable docility with little aerodynamic warning except for the distinct bangs as the automatic slats opened. From one of the all-up stalls I let the aircraft have its head in a dive, and the acceleration, although smooth, was impressive but not exceptional.

On reducing speed on entering the circuit for landing, the slats snapped out at 300 km/h (185 mph) just before I lowered the undercarriage at 260 km/h (160 mph) and the flaps to 20 degrees, and then fully down at 280 km/h (142 mph), which gave a nose-down trim change. The final approach was made at 200 km/h (125 mph) with a considerable amount of tail-heavy trim, and on crossing the airfield boundary at 185 km/h (115 mph) and cutting the throttle the nose started to drop and required a fair amount of backward movement on the stick to effect a three-point touchdown at 160 km/h (100 mph). The landing runout was quite straight-forward.

The La-7 was to me a complete revelation with regard to its handling characteristics and performance, which were quite superb. It had the qualities necessary for a fine combat fighter, but not the equipment. Its firepower and sighting arrangements were below par, its wooden construction would have withstood little punishment, the pilot was poorly protected, and the blind flying and navigation instrumentation was appallingly basic.

Having flown nine contemporary Russian front-line aircraft I began to understand how the Luftwaffe fighter pilots on the Eastern Front clocked up such huge victory scores, but in the case of the La-7 they would have to work hard for success.

Chapter 33
Lockheed Hudson

The Hudson was originally derived from the Lockheed 14 and built to the order of the British Government as a military conversion of the Type 14 transport which first flew on 29th July 1937. In all, six versions were delivered to the RAF, the majority of which were ferried across the Atlantic from the Lockheed factory site in Burbank, California, from the end of 1940. Its introduction into Coastal Command in May 1939 was far from auspicious, because the Anson crews found the Hudson a hot ship after their own obsolescent but docile aeroplanes,

and many accidents occurred during conversion training, mainly because the American aircraft was not easy to land.

The Hudson was a mid-wing twin-engined general reconnaissance mono-plane with a span of 65 ft 6 in, a length of 44 ft 4 in and a height of 11 ft 10½ in. It was powered by two Wright Cyclone or Pratt & Whitney Twin Wasp radial engines driving Hamilton-Standard constant-speed air-screws. It carried five crew and was armed with two fixed forward-firing machine-guns, a rotatable turret with two guns in the after end of the fuselage near the tailplane

The Lockheed Hudson – a real swinger.

with its twin rudders, and a retractable prone machine-gun position beneath the fuselage. There was internal stowage for bombs in the fuselage.

The handling characteristics of the Hudson in flight were generally satisfactory except for wing-dropping at the stall, but the landing offered difficulties inherently due to the large Fowler flaps between ailerons and fuselage on the 65 ft 6 in wing span. These flaps slid back 42 inches in streamline guides, and the ailerons were interconnected to droop with the flaps. There were low-drag slots in each wingtip in front of the ailerons.

The lowering of the flaps gave a very strong nose-down change of trim which resulted in a steep approach attitude at 80 mph. When it came to the hold-off, the control wheel had to be moved fully back at a precise rate to avoid ballooning or a wheel landing, which could cause bad porpoising if absolutely the correct attitude for touchdown at 72 mph was not obtained. On the runout there was a strong tendency to swing, which was aggravated by the fact that the Fowler flaps blanked the rudders, making them ineffective, and by the very poor brake control position. In crosswind conditions the landing had to be made in a tail-high attitude and with the control column pushed forward as speed fell off in order to keep the tailwheel off the ground for as long as possible, because once the tail was on the ground the rudders were blanked and a vicious swing could develop.

Experiments were made at the RAE to assess the tactical value of fitting a tail parachute to enable a Hudson to descend rapidly to 50–100 ft and execute a successful attack on a U-boat, having approached from heights up to 5,000 ft or unobserved in cloud cover.

The aircraft used for the trials was Hudson V AM753, powered by 2×1,200 hp Pratt & Whitney R-1830-67 14-cylinder engines. A 7 ft diameter parachute packed in a cotton snatch bag was loaded into a container built into the port side at the aft end of the fuselage. The parachute was attached to a towing cable which was secured by a release hook to the stern of the fuselage. A pilot control in the cockpit enabled release of the parachute, which did not open until the cable was at its fullest extent behind the aircraft. The same pilot's lever also controlled jettisoning after operation.

Comparative dive attacks were made from heights of 1,000 to 3,000 ft at 1,000 ft intervals, all into a wind velocity of 15–20 mph, with engines throttled right back and bomb doors opened at the beginning of the attack and kept open until the attack had been delivered. Speeds of 140 knots were not exceeded before opening the parachute, and an angle of dive of 40 degrees was not exceeded with the parachute open. The aircraft with the parachute attached was quite manoeuvrable and turns could be made easily. After pull-out from the dives, the parachute was jettisoned and level attacks carried out from 100 to 200 yards from the target at a height of 100 ft.

The tests showed that dive attacks initiated at heights up to 8,000 ft were practicable with the parachute, and the airspeed did not exceed 170 knots. Also they could be carried out in just about half the time it took without parachute from heights above 4,000 ft, but for attacks initiated below 4,000 ft the time advantage gradually began to depreciate as the start height was lowered. For example, the times from 8,000 ft were 135 sec without parachute and 70 sec with, and from 3,000 ft were 36 sec and 28 sec respectively.

To me it was surprising how low the pull-out with parachute attached could be initiated, a height of 300 ft being possible for dives over 25 degrees. In the event of failure of the parachute to release, which never happened in the trials, level flight could be maintained at 2,250 rpm and 35 in boost at 100 knots indicated air speed with the bomb doors shut. With bomb doors open, full boost and revs. were necessary to maintain height.

In conclusion, the trials were deemed successful and a recommendation made by

The Cyclone-engined version of the Hudson.

RAE to the Air Staff that use of the tail parachute with the Hudson had great possibilities in anti-submarine operations, although I am not aware if it was in fact ever used operationally. Certainly Hudsons were very successful on anti-shipping patrols, being involved in the destruction or surrender of 24 U-boats in a period of 26 months.

To my mind, however, the most astonishing use made of the Hudson was in No 161 Squadron, dropping Allied agents in enemy-occupied territory, and involving landings at night in French fields indicated by Resistance groups. That was hazardous work indeed, without the added aggravation of the aircraft's landing idiosyncrasies.

Chapter 34
Lockheed P2V Neptune

arly in 1949 a request was received at
RAE Farnborough for an assessment
to be made of the feasibility of
landing a Neptune on the deck of a
'Midway' class aircraft carrier. In view of
my experience with deck landing trials
with British twin-engined aircraft I was
inevitably given this project. At the same
time Aerodynamics Department at RAE
tasked me with investigating the operation
of the varicam (variable camber) control
fitted to the tailplane of this aircraft.

The P2V was the US Navy's new post-
Second World War land-based patrol

aeroplane, and it came into prominence
when an XP2V-1 named *Truculent Turtle*
took off from Perth, Australia, on 29th
September 1946 at a weight of 83,000 lb
using Jet Assisted Take-Off (JATO) and 55
hr 17 min later landed at Columbus, Ohio,
on 1st October, having flown a record
distance of 11,235.6 miles.

This flight was not just a stunt, but was a
serious operational trial for a special
purpose. The US Navy started to consider
in 1945 the concept of a long-range carrier-
based nuclear strike capability, and the
Neptune was the only naval aircraft which

The very long range Lockheed Neptune.

could carry the then state-of-the-art nuclear bomb weighing 10,000 lb and possibly get this load off a carrier deck. With a wing span of 100 ft, a length of 78 ft, a height of 28 ft and a take-off weight of 60,000 lb this would be the biggest and heaviest aeroplane ever to leave a carrier deck.

Two P2V-2s were craned from barges on to the flight deck of the USS *Coral Sea* and flown off successfully with the aid of JATO bottles attached to the aircraft. To develop this test into an operational capability, the US Navy ordered 12 specially modified P2V-3Cs, equipped with special high-altitude engines and with a fuel tankage of 4,400 gallons, almost double that of the standard P2V-3. This variant was to be capable of carrying a 14-kiloton atomic bomb weighing 9,000 lb, of the type dropped at Hiroshima.

The Neptune flown into Farnborough by the US Navy was P2V-2A serial number 39344, powered by two 2,500 hp Wright Duplex Cyclone radial engines. The pilot who flew the aircraft in gave me a brief on the carrier trials that had taken place to date, and said it was proposed to fit an arrester hook for landing on the new flush-deck type aircraft carriers then under construction.

The P2V-2A as prepared for my flight on 10th January 1949 was at an all-up weight of 54,000 lb, which was the maximum weight for landing. My first impression on entering the cockpit was one of organised chaos, there being so many dials, levers and switches. However, a lengthy brief by my co-pilot put order into the chaos.

The take-off was very straightforward and easy, it being possible to raise the nosewheel off the ground at 60 knots and unstick in a very short distance at 80 knots, using 10 degrees of flap. At full take-off power of 53 in Hg of manifold pressure and 2,800 rpm there was not much impression of rapid acceleration.

The safety speed in the condition flown was 110 knots with the undercarriage retracted and one airscrew windmilling. Actually I could hold the aircraft straight and level at 95 knots, using full strength pressure on the rudder and about half aileron, but height could not be gained at more than about 50 ft/min at that speed. My utmost physical effort could not apply full rudder in such circumstances, but with full rudder trim wound on and two-thirds aileron I could hold the aircraft straight and level down to 85 knots, at which speed there was the onset of buffeting.

The inaccessible location of the rudder trim wheel at the base of the pedestal between the two pilots' seats, combined with the fact that it was low-geared and therefore slow in manual operation, made it hopeless for emergency use, although an engine failure below 110 knots would have been more than an emergency, it would have been a potential disaster.

After a climb to 5,000 ft which showed the aircraft to have very positive stability, it was levelled off into cruising flight at 165 knots before testing the varicam control for effectiveness.

The tailplane of the Neptune was divided into two sections, the rear portion being moveable and also carrying at its trailing edge very narrow-chord elevators. Variable camber was thus imparted to the tailplane, and was controllable by the pilot from a toggle switch located on the cockpit control pedestal. The object of this arrangement was to give the pilot a light elevator control in normal flight, and also provide him with a trimming device which had the dual purpose of increasing elevator power at the extremes of the speed range.

In the cruise at 165 knots the varicam setting to trim was 0 degrees, and the test of its effectiveness was begun by setting the varicam to its nose-down setting limit of 4 degrees and observing that the pull force to maintain level flight was about 120 lb (my physical limit), with the control wheel position about 2 inches aft of the original trimmed cruising position.

With the varicam then reset to 0 degrees the aircraft was flown throughout the speed range from the stall to its limiting dive speed of 300 knots without encountering any abnormally heavy stick forces. The feel of the other two controls at cruising speeds gave an impression of very bad harmony of control, for the ailerons were moderately heavy and the rudder very heavy.

To sum up, I felt that the varicam undoubtedly succeeded in giving the aircraft a very light elevator control within a liberal range of the speed for which the setting was chosen, but it had two obvious faults. Firstly, the rate of operation (¾ degree/sec) was too slow for such a large aircraft, and, secondly, the cockpit control was badly positioned, since it should undoubtedly have been on the control wheel by the pilot's left thumb.

Reverting to the deck landing assessment part of the tests, I started a series of stalls at 5,000 ft. The all-down stall with the engines throttled back occurred almost without warning at 79 knots. Actually considerable elevator buffeting set in at 80 knots and then was immediately followed by a modest starboard wing drop.

The effect of power on the stall was tried with the engines set to 20 in Hg of manifold pressure, and this reduced the all-down stalling speed to 68 knots. Buffeting started at 75 knots, together with a tendency for the starboard wing to drop. These character- istics became accentuated, particularly the buffeting, until the nose finally dropped away and the aircraft remained laterally level although about a quarter port aileron was applied at that stage.

The next step was a series of landings, starting with a normal airfield landing at 100 knots without moving the varicam from the 0 degrees setting. There was very little change of trim with lowering of the undercarriage and flaps, what there was being slightly nose-up. The hold-off required a fairly strong pull force over a fairly wide arc of travel. It was altogether a very straightforward procedure, but immediately the main wheels contacted the runway the aircraft pitched on to its nosewheel. A second landing at 95 knots using the varicam during hold-off required only a very light pull force over a very small arc of travel, and even as speed fell off on the landing run the nosewheel could easily be held off the ground down to 60 knots.

I next tried a simulated deck landing at 85 knots using 32 in Hg of manifold pressure to regulate the rate of descent to 400 ft/min, but the aileron control although light was unacceptably ineffective, and the elevator control, although also light, was just marginally effective.

In the USA one of the special P2V-3Cs, serial number 122969, was equipped with an arrester hook and a considerable number of landings were made into the dummy deck arrester gear at NATC Patuxent River. Finally a touch-and-go landing was made aboard USS *Franklin D Roosevelt* in the autumn of 1949, but the US Navy made its final decision not to risk a shipboard arrested deck landing.

The Neptune was a very unimpressive aircraft to fly, being sluggish in the air both from the point of view of handling and performance, except in the matter of range, which was outstanding, as evidenced by the many distance records it achieved. Certainly it will be remembered as the first aeroplane to give the US Navy nuclear strike capability, as well as for setting a world long-distance record which stood for almost twenty years.

Chapter 35
McDonnell F2H Banshee

During my spell of duty as a test pilot in Flight Test at Patuxent River Naval Air Test Center in the early 1950s, one of my projects was the McDonnell F2H-2 and F2H-3 Banshee single-seat naval fighter. This was one of America's early jet aircraft, and was of orthodox mid-wing design layout with a span of 45 ft, a length of 40 ft 2 in and an all-up weight of 19,950 lb, with a maximum weight of 22,084 lb.

The neat-looking Banshee was powered by two 3,250 lb static thrust axial-flow Westinghouse J34-WE-34 turbojets, and the F2H-2 had a fuel capacity of 1,277 US gallons, including two 200-gallon jettisonable wing-tip tanks. Armament was 4×20 mm nose cannon, and a 2,000 lb bomb load or 8×5 in rockets could be carried externally.

The elevators each had a pilot-operated trim tab and a spring tab. The ailerons were hydraulically power-boosted at a 16:1 ratio, and each had a balance tab adjustable on the ground, while there was also a pilot-operated trim tab on the left aileron. A combination trim and anti-balance tab was installed on the rudder, the trim tab being pilot-operated.

The F2H-2 Banshee naval fighter.

The landing flaps were of a conventional split type divided into six parts, and were attached to the outer and centre wing panels. The two-position speed brakes were of the perforated upright panel type, emerging scissorwise on upper and lower outer wing surfaces, and were actuated by a thumb switch on the throttle lever. Engine starting on this model was sluggish, and tended to give excessive jet pipe temperatures, sometimes requiring shut-down.

Taxying the Banshee was very straight-forward, with excellent pilot view. Take-off was simple with reasonable acceleration, but after lift-off the undercarriage (8 secs) and flaps (7 secs) were slow to retract. The rate of climb was mediocre for a fighter, taking 11.5 min to 30,000 ft and then falling off badly to take 19 min to 40,000 ft. The service ceiling was 46,000 ft.

In flight, longitudinal stability character-istics were good, but the manoeuvring control force of 3 lb per 'g' at 415 knots at 10,000 ft was dangerous for an aircraft with such low limit acceleration load factors (6.4 'g' with a design ultimate factor of 1.5).

The maximum rate of roll was 120 degrees per second at 260 knots, decreasing substantially with increase in airspeed. The ailerons barely self-centred, and lateral stick-free stability was negative, which made instrument flying a chore. With hydraulic boost off, lateral control was just good enough for airfield landings with a symmetric fuel load.

The aircraft snaked badly in rough air, the lateral-directional oscillations being of short period and large amplitude, thus affording a bad gun platform. It was eventually fitted with a yaw damper as a cure.

The limiting tactical Mach number was 0.80, at which value strong buffeting

The F2H-3 Banshee on catapult trials at NATC, Patuxent River.

started and was accompanied by a slight lateral oscillation, both building up in intensity to a safe flight limiting Mach number of 0.84. With nose-down elevator trim tab deflections greater than 10 degrees, an aerodynamic spring tab-trim interaction could be developed during high Mach number dive pull-outs at low altitude. The interaction produced rather a severe elevator buffet which could be dissipated almost immediately by decreasing the nose-down trim tab deflection or by extending the speed brakes.

The speed brakes were very effective in producing deceleration, and their extension gave only a slight nose-down pitching moment which could be counter-acted by a 5 lb pull force throughout the speed range. Unfortunately there was a heavy buffet when these brakes were open, which would ruin sighting in combat.

Stall characteristics were excellent, with the stick shaker cutting in some 11 knots above the stall and beginning to buzz heavily 4½ knots before the stall, which consisted of a nose-down pitch and slight drop of either wing. These characteristics were the same whether the aircraft was in the clean or the landing configuration.

The aircraft had a jerky, porpoising spin but recovered in half a turn when the controls were centralised. The use of full opposite rudder usually resulted in reversing the direction of the spin.

The deck landing characteristics of the F2H-2 were very good. Lowering of the flaps gave a very strong nose-up trim change which was to some degree neutralised by the forward movement of the control column under the influence of a flap-operated bungee. At normal arrested landing weights the approach speed was 110 knots, and use of the speed brakes, which were actuated by a thumb switch on the throttle lever, just after crossing the carrier's stern gave a very positive deck contact.

Handling characteristics with asymmetric power were good, and single-engine deck landings were a practical proposition.

Even a wave-off could be taken 'in the groove' provided the fuel load was below 250 US gallons.

The top speed of the F2H-2 was 498 knots TAS at sea level, and on one engine was 393 knots TAS at sea level. It had a range of 1,590 nm at 410 knots TAS at 42,000 ft.

In summary, this was a mediocre straight-wing jet fighter inferior in almost every respect to the contemporary Gloster Meteor IV. It was, however, immensely popular with US Navy pilots as it gave them a fairly carefree introduction into the use of carrier-borne jet aircraft.

The Banshee was developed from the FH-1 Phantom, which was the first naval aircraft ever to be built by McDonnell Aircraft Corporation, and also the first jet aircraft to land on an American carrier, on 21st July 1946, almost eight months after a similar event in Britain. Only one squadron of Phantoms was operated, but the Banshee operated extensively in Korea as a fighter-bomber and in the photo-reconnaissance role, although it never engaged in combat with North Korean MiGs.

The F2H-3 model was an all-weather development of the F2H-2. The main changes were a fuselage increased in length by 6 ft to house large fuel tanks and electronics equipment; the wing span decreased by 3 ft 3 in; the tailplane relocated lower and farther aft, and incorporating 10 degrees dihedral; tailplane and fin thickness reduced from 11 to 9 per cent; and internal fuel capacity increased by 225 US gallons. Wing-tip fuel tanks were not normally fitted. There were also two major equipment changes – a complete new armament installation with Mk.12 guns instead of M3 guns, and relocated from the nose to the side of the aircraft; and an AN/APQ41 radar and P-3 autopilot fitted. Furthermore, a 4,500 lb bomb load could be carried.

With the same engines as the F2H-2, the normal all-up weight of the F2H-3 was 21,005 lb, with a maximum weight of 26,165 lb. Thus the power/weight ratio of the F2H-3 was worse than that of the earlier model, and the wing loading had increased significantly. The overall effects would be revealed in the flight testing.

There was also a major change to the control system, in that both the elevators and ailerons had irreversible hydraulic power applied to them with artificial feel provided. Both had manual reversion, and the ailerons had an automatic ratio changer which increased the stick-to-aileron mechanical advantage whenever the hydraulic pressure in the aileron power control system dropped to 300 lb/in². Accompanying the increase in mechanical advantage was a corresponding decrease in aileron throw by a half. The artificial feel provided for the ailerons was supplied by a double-acting spring cartridge, so the force felt by the pilot was independent of airspeed. The elevator artificial feel system, however, gave the pilot a reference stick force proportional to airspeed. This force was obtained from ram or pitot air pressure acting on a diaphragm within a bellows. The bellows force was balanced against a spring force by means of the trim bell-crank to obtain zero stick forces. Movement of the control stick would then upset this balanced condition, causing a resistance to stick movement proportional to the degree of stick deflection. A viscous damper was incorporated in the system to prevent abrupt fore and aft stick movements and resulting accelerations that could overload the structure. A 5 lb per 'g' bob-weight was attached to the control stick.

The control stick trim switch controlled the artificial feel systems and the aileron trim tab, whilst the elevator trim tabs were positioned automatically by an idler bending beam incorporated in the elevator control system between the power cylinder and the elevator hinge bell-crank. This automatic feature prevented a severe change in longitudinal trim requirements in the event of an hydraulic system failure by reducing elevator hinge moments to zero. It did this by deflecting and actuating micro-switches which drove the elevator trim tab motor. An elevator trim-tab

override switch was provided to permit the pilot to position the tab should the automatic system fail, and prior to take-off before the equaliser idler became effective.

Entry into the cockpit was better than on the F2H-2. There were, however, drawbacks in the cockpit layout in that the aileron and elevator power control switches could not be reached by the pilot without first releasing the shoulder harness; also the airspeed indicator glare shield obscured readings between 100 and 150 knots, the crucial range for deck landing.

Engine starting was greatly improved over that of the F2H-2 by the addition of positive starter and ignition switches. Taxying was easy, with a superb view, and take-off characteristics were excellent, although the elevators were so powerful that care had to be taken not to rotate the aircraft to an angle of attack greater than that required for maximum lift, otherwise a condition of excessive drag would result, with a deteriorative effect on take-off distance. Care had also to be taken not to retract the undercarriage immediately upon take-off, as cycling of the landing gear doors caused a slight loss of lift and an increase in drag which caused the aeroplane to settle slightly.

Longitudinal stability and control characteristics were very good, and the stick force of 5½ lb per 'g' throughout the speed range at 10,000 ft at mid CG was excellent, since the model was built to the normal US fighter structural yield load of 7½ 'g', as opposed to 6.4 'g' for the earlier Banshee models.

Failure of the elevator powered control system resulted in negligible out-of-trim force change by virtue of the efficient automatic trimming device.

Lateral stability and control characteristics were generally good. The maximum rate of roll was 150 degrees per second at 350 knots, which was rather low, and it decreased substantially with increase in airspeed. Aileron self-centering was positive with lateral control power on or off. By providing an electric motor, which trimmed both the aileron trim tab and the feel spring, aileron hinge moments were kept near zero, thus preventing high rolling moments in event of hydraulic power failure. Dihedral effect was low.

Directional snaking characteristics were unsatisfactory in normal cruising or high speed flight with the yaw damper off, but were improved to a very satisfactory degree by the excellent yaw damper installed in the aircraft.

The manoeuvring stick force per 'g' was about 5.5 lb, and the harmony of control was excellent with power on and satisfactory with control power off. The failure of only one of the systems with the other remaining operative resulted in poor harmony of control.

The F2H-3 had a safe flight limit Mach number of 0.97, but its tactical limit Mach number was about 0.85. Airframe buffet started lightly at 0.84 and increased in intensity up to 0.91, when it started to decrease until at 0.97 it was about the same intensity as at 0.85. Lateral unsteadiness set in at 0.91 and developed into right-wing heaviness at 0.96. Elevator effectiveness deteriorated gradually beyond 0.87, where the drag rose sharply.

Recovery from dives required only moderate control forces. Use of the speed brakes, which extended fully in 1.3 sec at speeds up to 0.85 indicated Mach number, caused moderate airframe buffet and a very slight nose-down pitch. Deceleration was satisfactory.

A vortex generator installation was tried on the F2H-3 with excellent results, in that it reduced high Mach number buffet, improved the longitudinal trim characteristics and eliminated wing heaviness to such an extent that it raised the tactical limit Mach number to 0.90. The installation consisted of 94 thin metal sections mounted normal to the surface of each wing in a single row along the 25.3157% wing chord line, extending from the outboard edge of the aileron balance tab to the intersection of the wing and fuselage.

The generators were spaced about two inches apart and protruded half an inch from the surface of the wing. The chord of each generator was about half an inch, and the thickness was 0.03 in. Each vortex generator was installed at an angle of attack of 20 degrees, with adjacent generators arranged to produce vortices rotating in opposite directions.

Stalling characteristics were mild, and there was adequate stall warning. As in the F2H-2, artificial stall warning was provided by a stick shaker which operated only when the wing flaps were extended. The stall warning margin was approximately 15 knots in the powered approach configuration, and was about 5 knots too high for carrier approaches.

The runway and deck landing characteristics were virtually the same as those of the earlier model, although the F2H-3 had improved catapulting behaviour owing to the extendable nosewheel strut. The F2H-3's folded span was 18 ft 5 in, an increase of 1 ft 8½ in over that of its predecessor.

Single-engine flight characteristics were good, and single-engine deck landings were straightforward except that no wave-off could be accepted in the late stages of approach.

The top speed was 507 knots TAS at sea level. Time to climb to 30,000 ft was 10 min, and to 40,000 ft was 18.5 min. Range was 1,150 nm at 395 knots TAS at 40,000 ft.

The F2H-3 was quite an outstanding aircraft as regards stability and control, and was a big improvement in this respect over the F2H-2. It had gained slightly in performance over the F2H-2, except for range, and had gained substantially over it in high Mach number capabilities.

The Banshee 3 saw some service in Korea, where it was largely used in the ground-attack and photographic reconnaissance roles. It was very popular with pilots and had a very good record as a carrier aircraft. Personally I enjoyed flying this amiable aeroplane, which conveyed a feeling of docility combined with nippiness, making it a pleasure to handle.

Chapter 36
Miles Master II

The Miles M.19 Master II advanced trainer was virtually a re-engined version of the underpowered Master I, which had been fitted with the Rolls-Royce Kestrel XXX 12-cylinder Vee water-cooled engine. The more powerful Bristol Mercury XX 9-cylinder radial air-cooled engine of 870 hp not only enhanced the performance of the aeroplane, but changed its appearance. The Mark I was somewhat of Hurricane looks, while the Mark II with its clipped wings seemed chunkier and more like a souped-up Harvard.

This was a wooden aeroplane with stressed plywood skin, and had gull wings with hydraulically-operated split trailing-edge flaps, and a retractable undercarriage with wheels that turned and then retracted backwards. It was very representative in size of contemporary fighters, with a span of 35 ft 9 in, a length of 29 ft 6 in and a height of 9 ft 5 in. Its empty weight was 4,130 lb, and loaded weight 5,312 lb. Top speed was 255 mph at 10,000 ft.

From a handling point of view the Master II was fairly representative of what a naval fighter could have been in the 1940s, so it was chosen for an interesting experiment in relation to such fighters. The aircraft chosen, DL185, was in fact a hybrid, having a Master II fuselage with the old Mk.I wings of 39 ft span with squared tips. Spring tab wide-chord ailerons of short length were fitted, with the primary purpose of allowing larger-area flaps to be fitted to any wing thus equipped. Such an application would of course be of particular benefit to naval aircraft, and the behaviour of the ailerons was of especial interest at low speeds. In any case, a speed restriction of 200 mph was placed on this experimental aircraft for structural considerations.

I made a flight on DL185 on 5th June 1945 and while making my control checks on the ground I found a very noticeable large moment of inertia in the ailerons, but this disappeared completely in flight, probably owing to the very weak spring used on the tab. The rate of roll at normal cruising speeds was an improvement over that of the standard Master, and there seemed to be very little increase of stick force from 100 mph to 200 mph, so the lateral control was definitely light. The aircraft was, however, laterally unstable (stick free), although the stick self-centered when released after displacement.

The all-up stall occurred at 79 mph and with no warning. The left wing dropped sharply, and though aileron control was positive right down to the stall, large stick movements could produce a premature stall up to about 84 mph. When the stall did occur the nose dipped with the stalled wing and so the speed rose at once, and only a 2 or 3 mph increase in indicated airspeed was sufficient to regain lateral control and raise the wing.

The all-down stall occurred at 58 mph without warning other than a slight lateral twitch. The right wing dropped gently and again the nose dipped sufficiently to give a slight rise in airspeed and allowed lateral control to be regained. The ailerons were still effective right down to the stall, although they were definitely sluggish and lacking in feel. At the stall there was about one inch of upfloat on the ailerons at the trailing edge, but this progressively decreased until there was none at 200 mph.

For the purpose of comparison I flew

The nippy Miles Master II.

standard Master II DM352 on 7th June, which of course had rounded wing tips. It proved heavier on the ailerons with a slower rate of roll, and there was a noticeable build-up in force with increase in speed from 100 to 200 mph. The lateral stability (stick free) was neutral, although the stick self-centered when released after displacement.

The all-up stall at 77 mph and all-down at 61 mph displayed the same characteristics as on DL185, although the ailerons seemed crisper, and certainly had more feel close to the stall. The interesting point, however, was that the all-down stalling speed was higher in spite of the increased wing area of this aircraft, and the significance was that the stall occurred on the ailerons on both Masters.

It was decided to investigate the stall characteristics further on both aircraft by making a series of powered stalls. The behaviour of the standard aircraft was more vicious, but in both cases the stall was entirely on the ailerons and the lateral control was less effective close to the stall with engine on than with engine off; consequently the wing could not be picked up until quite an appreciable increase in speed occurred. In that respect, however, the wide-chord ailerons showed up slightly better than the standard ailerons.

Approaches to the aerodrome were made in very bumpy weather at 85 mph with power on, and the hybrid Master was very difficult to control laterally, whereas the standard Master felt more secure although both required a high work rate.

My conclusion was that the wide-chord ailerons were not good enough in their current form for deck-landing on an aircraft carrier, but offered distinct possibilities as a rather better-than-usual application of spring tabs to ailerons. In fact I had at that time found only one case of really good spring tab ailerons for deck landing, namely those of the Grumman Hellcat III, which in its earlier marks without spring tabs had basically good aileron control anyway.

Chapter 37
Miles Oddities

Magister with Trailer Wing

Early in the Second World War the concepts of the slip-wing and trailer wing were experimented with on a Hurricane and Miles Magister respectively. Fundamentally both concepts had the same objective, namely to attach a jettisonable auxiliary wing to an aircraft to increase its lift and its payload. Normally the wing would only be jettisoned in an emergency, when more speed was required.

The trailer wing experiment was allocated to RAE Farnborough, and the aircraft used was a standard RAF elementary Magister trainer, L8326. The tests started on 12th May 1941, and were carried out at Boscombe Down because of the longer take-off space available.

The trailer consisted of an aerofoil of 25 ft span hinged on the rear spar of the Magister by means of release points and connected by rigid booms. The trailer had a two-wheeled castoring undercarriage and endplate fins fitted to the aerofoil. The Magister itself had a wing span of 33 ft 10 in.

Taxying tests showed that the combination of rather inferior brakes on the

The author with Magister in 1939.

The author with Magister at Sydenham, Belfast in 1939.

main wheels, three castoring rear wheels (including the tail-wheel) and only a normal rudder to cope with the extra keel surface of the end plates all contributed to make steering on the ground virtually impossible. A few long hops were made, and these emphasised the critical nature of the directional control, whereas the longitudinal control was satisfactory and there was only a slight deterioration in aileron control.

The Magister may seem an odd choice for such an experiment, but it must be remembered that when it first appeared in 1937, powered by only a 130 hp de Havilland Gipsy Major I, it was faster than the equivalent biplane trainer and yet had a landing speed of only 42 mph.

For the first flights the Magister's rudder area was increased by 30%, so that the aircraft combination could now be taken off straight with full engine power, but using almost full left rudder. In level flight a maximum speed of only 80 mph could be attained, and although the trailer behaved very well longitudinally, control was not too good about the other two axes. Laterally, the ailerons were heavy and rather ineffective, and when bank was fairly rapidly applied there was a difference of about 10 degrees between the mainplanes and the trailer. Directionally, the control was very poor and just marginally acceptable for the tests.

The next stage was to carry 2×110 lb bombs on the trailer, but this produced a form of directional snaking during take-off which was uncontrollable, probably due to oscillatory moments being set up in the trailer during the unstick process, so the take-off had to be aborted. This problem was cured by making the rear wheels lockable to prevent shimmying. The trailer payload was then increased to 4×110 lb bombs, but again uncontrollable swing was experienced and the trailer took charge of the aircraft, swinging it through 50 degrees and causing it to charge into obstructions, with resulting serious damage.

For the final stage of the tests, rudders were fitted to the endplates of the trailer to improve directional control. However, the taxying characteristics were still bad, and indeed on occasions when a turn was attempted the trailer would take charge and turn the aircraft through 360 degrees, finally causing it to go backwards. This was probably due to the castor angle limits of the trailer wheels being too great, and also being undamped.

For the first few yards of the take-off run the machine had to be kept straight by use of the brakes. Then, with a few mph of speed built up, a modicum of directional control could be picked up on the rudders, and once 20 mph was reached there was little risk of directional control being lost.

In flight in smooth air the trailer maintained its correct position, but if bumps were encountered it would pitch and yaw continuously. In calm air, turns with up to 60 degrees of bank could be made with the trailer behaving satisfactorily, although the lateral stick forces were high.

In a dive to 120 mph the trailer kept good position until bumps were encountered at low altitude, when it began to pitch and yaw so severely that there was a grave risk of it taking charge of the aircraft.

From these tests it was apparent that flying with the trailer wing was a bit of a knife-edge operation, particularly on take-off and in bumpy weather, and for those reasons the experiments were not continued.

Magister with McLaren Undercarriage
When I was in the Fleet Air Arm's Service Trials Unit at Arbroath in 1942 I flew Magister P6456, equipped with an undercarriage capable of being rotated through 45 degrees on either side of the centre line of the aircraft by means of a crank handle, angle indicator, and lock. The obvious purpose behind this invention was to ease the problems created in crosswind landings.

My flights were undertaken on 16th and 17th September when a steady wind of 20 mph was blowing, and with a choice of three runways quite a number of computations were possible to give the desired crosswind components for the tests.

On the first day I gradually worked up to 30 degree crosswind landings and found these quite easy and comfortable to execute. On the second day I moved up the scale to the full 45 degree crosswind landings, and although these were effective they were neither easy nor comfortable to execute. It was difficult to crab the aircraft accurately on to the runway at the larger drift angles, and after touchdown braking had to be very judiciously applied to prevent side loads on the undercarriage if the fuselage was not aligned dead into wind.

My conclusion was that the weight of the equipment did not justify the end. It was as likely to cause accidents as prevent them at crosswind angles above 30 degrees, and really could only be applicable to light aircraft whose pilots were usually comparatively inexperienced. Verdict – nice try but no dice.

Miles M.18 Mk.II
This little two-seat trainer was a development of the Mk.I, of which only the prototype was built and was not very successful. The Mk.II prototype had the fin and rudder moved forward 22 in, was fitted with slats and had a more powerful engine, namely the 150 hp Blackburn Cirrus Major III. It was sent to RAE Farnborough for investigation of its stalling characteristics and suspected spiral instability – the inability to trim the aircraft into a steady sideslip owing to control deficiencies.

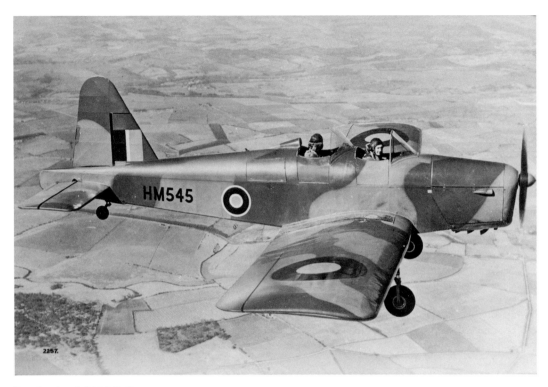

Production M.18 Mk.II.

I first flew the Mk.II, JN703, on 18th May 1944. It had a span of 31 ft, a length of 24 ft 10 in, an empty weight of 1,306 lb and a loaded weight of 1.925 lb. In flight the control deficiencies became immediately apparent. The ailerons were fairly light, but their feel and effectiveness was somewhat lost by the large amount of friction throughout their range of movement. The effect of the slats in the open position (achieved by mechanical handle) was to cause a slight lag in response, which developed into sluggishness when the flaps were lowered (also by mechnical handle). The elevators were light and effective in their range, but inadequate to control the aircraft with slats open and flaps down under power-off conditions. However, the inadequacy of the rudder control was the limiting factor in carrying out normal manoeuvres such as sideslips and steep turns, and the rudder was almost completely useless as an aid to taxying.

I found that the aircraft could not be stalled with the slats open, irrespective of whether the flaps were up or down, even with the stick right back and elevator trim wound fully aft. With the slats closed, the flaps-up stall occurred sharply at 55 mph after some buffeting warning, while with flaps down the right wing dropped very sharply and without warning, putting the aircraft into a steep right-hand dive.

As a result of these tests the RAE recommended modifications to the aircraft, which were presumably incorporated by Miles, as it received its civilian Certificate of Airworthiness on 29th August 1946. It then went on to a distinguished air racing career, winning the Goodyear Trophy in 1956 at 130 mph, the Osram Cup in 1957 at 136 mph, and the King's Cup in 1961 at 142 mph.

Miles M.38 Messenger.

Miles M.38 Messenger at Sea

While in the Service Trials Unit at Arbroath, I was suddenly asked to check out whether a light four-seat aircraft destined for Army Co-operation duties could be safely operated on an escort carrier on an *ad hoc* basis. The aeroplane proved to be the prototype Miles Messenger, U-0223, which was duly delivered to Machrihanish airfield, from which I was already conducting acceptance trials with a Grumman Martlet IV on the escort carriers *Attacker* and *Hunter* in the Firth of Clyde in mid-June 1943.

The M.38 was a development of the M.28 and was similarly of wooden construction, but incorporated several detail changes. Miles non-retractable auxiliary aerofoil flaps were hinged aft of and slightly below the wing trailing edge, between the fuselage and ailerons. Slotted ailerons were interconnected with the flaps and drooped when the flaps were lowered. A third central fin and rudder was added to ensure maximum directional control right down to the stall. Finally, an elementary form of single-strut undercarriage with Miles oleo-pneumatic articulated suspension was fitted, together with an oleo-sprung self-centering tailwheel. The aircraft was equipped with dual controls.

The M.38 had a wing span of 36 ft 2 in, a length of 23 ft 9 in, a height of 7 ft 6 in, an empty weight of 1,360 lb and a loaded weight of 2,400 lb. It was powered by a 140 hp D.H. Gipsy Major ID four-cylinder in-line air-cooled engine.

A quick check on the flaps-down stalling speed gave an absurd 28 mph. In consequence I decided on a carrier approach speed of 35 mph to allow sufficient control in the turbulent wake off the carrier's flight deck.

When I arrived over *Hunter* on 22nd June the combined windspeed over the deck (the carrier's speed plus the speed of the local wind) was 30 knots, and since this was equal to my intended approach speed I had no alternative but to open up the engine and drive the M.38 on to the deck at about 45 mph. Even then I felt I was never going to catch up with the carrier. When I cut the throttle the aeroplane sat down gently and literally stood still on the deck. The take-off was just as ridiculous. I ran the aircraft up to full power on the brakes and then released them, holding the stick well back, and the M.38 ran about its own length and then went up like a lift. Certainly for landing the lateral control left something to be desired, but even so this was the idiot's ideal deck-landing aircraft.

Chapter 38
North American FJ-2 Fury

The FJ-1 Fury, of which only 33 were built, was the straight-winged forerunner of the swept-wing FJ-2, and was powered by a 3,820 lb static thrust General Electric J35-GE-2 axial-flow turbojet. It first flew on 27th November 1946, and was the last US Navy fighter to be armed with 6×0.5 in machine-guns.

The FJ-2 arose directly out of the success of the superb F-86 Sabre, of which the US Navy ordered three examples to be designated the XFJ-2. Of these, two prototypes were essentially navalised F-86Es,

and the first flight was made on 14th February 1952.

This low-wing, single-seat naval fighter had a span of 37 ft 1 in, a length of 37 ft 7 in, a normal weight of 16,122 lb and a maximum of 18,882 lb. Its armament was 4×20 mm cannon located in the forward fuselage, with 60 rounds per gun.

The FJ-2 was powered by a 6,090 lb static thrust General Electric J47-GE-27 axial-flow turbojet. The wings and tailplane were swept back 35 degrees, and the fuselage was fitted with a V-frame arrester hook and

The North American FJ-2 Fury on its carrier trials.

catapult points. The internal fuel capacity was 434 US gallons.

Longitudinal control was by means of the combined action of elevator and tailplane. The tailplane was adjustable for longitudinal trim, and automatic wing slats and fuselage mounted variable position speed brakes were fitted.

An irreversible constant-pressure hydraulic system powered the 'flying tail' and ailerons, and artificial spring feel was provided. An electrically powered alternative hydraulic system was provided to operate the controls if the normal system functioned incorrectly. Two hydraulic cylinders in tandem actuated the surface controls, each of these cylinders being hydraulically independent of the other so that loss of pressure to one cylinder did not affect the other. The primary control was an automatic electric transfer system, which automatically changed over to the alternative system if the normal system malfunctioned. The secondary electrical transfer system permitted the pilot to select either system for test or for operation. Electrical transfer to either system was prevented if the pressure in the selected system was below minimum operating pressure. The emergency transfer would, when actuated, mechanically position the transfer valves to select the alternative system regardless of the pressure in that system. A warning light on the instrument panel illuminated when the flight controls were operating on the alternative system.

The cockpit of the Fury was a delight, with a superb view and a logical instrument layout. The aircraft was easy to taxi, with its steerable nosewheel and positive braking. Altogether this felt a real pilot's aeroplane which was raring to go. Certainly it impressed on take-off with its acceleration, effective rudder and elevators, and shortish run to unstick. Once the wheels were retracted the Fury had an impressive rate of climb, taking 11 min to reach 40,000 ft.

In normal cruising flight the stability and control characteristics were generally excellent. The Fury had beautiful harmony of control with a stick force per 'g' of about 5 lb throughout the speed range at mid CG, while the lateral control was light with positive smooth centering. The maximum rate of roll was 208 degrees/sec at M=0.68 at 10,000 ft, and 223 degrees/sec at M=0.78 at 30,000 ft. The directional stability and control force and effectiveness were satisfactory, and it was more comfortable in rough air and was a better gun platform than the contemporary Banshee and Panther.

The high Mach number characteristics were good, with a good useable spread of high-altitude/high Mach number buffet boundary, which gave it excellent tactical manoeuvrability up to 35,000 ft.

The stall characteristics were excellent in all configurations, being mild and with a 6 knot airframe buffet warning of the imminent stall. Spinning was equally innocuous, with swift recovery using anti-spin action.

The early deck-landing trials with the XFJ-2 showed it to be a nice aircraft to control on the approach at 115 knots, but I found the view poor at that speed, although the aeroplane felt very safe to fly since little attention had to be paid to speed once it was trimmed into the final approach because of the strong positive static longitudinal stability. The view problem was cured on production aircraft by lowering the windshield and increasing flap angle from 38 to 45 degrees, thus giving a 2 degree reduction in incidence for the same lift coefficient.

The nosewheel oleo could be extended hydraulically from an external position to a total travel of 15½ in, and thus increased the static ground angle from 4 to 8 degrees for catapult launching, but a further 7 degrees dynamic longitudinal rotation was required by the pilot at the end of the power stroke for a clean get-away. To develop maximum lift coefficient a total incidence of 17 degrees was required. The hydraulic extending pressure was automatically released on retraction of the undercarriage or lowering of the arrester hook.

Catapulting was carried out during the shipboard trials to an AUW of 18,882 lb, but unsatisfactory dynamic response at the end of the catapult power stroke prevented full attainment of maximum lift coefficient, so launching was restricted to a windspeed of 35 knots over the deck. To overcome this latter fault a pneumatic nosewheel oleo extension was fitted to production models to give a total oleo travel of 12 in, thus providing some rebound energy at the end of the catapult power stroke and helping the pilot quickly to achieve the required angle of attack for maximum lift coefficient. The rigidity of the hydraulic extension prevented such nosewheel throw-off.

For shipboard operations the outer 7 ft of each wing folded upwards at right angles, giving a folded span of 22 ft 6 in, and a folded height of 15 ft 11 in.

Although not as fast as the F-86E, the Fury still had a useful turn of speed, reaching 596 knots at sea level. However, its range of 500 nm at 400 knots at 40,000 ft was a decided shortcoming. When two 200 US gallon external underwing drop tanks were fitted the XFJ-2 became inferior to the F9F-6 Panther in combat effectiveness owing to reduced climb performance (14.3 min to 35,000 ft), level flight performance and manoeuvring capabilities.

In its clean form the Fury was an excellent aeroplane to handle, but like the British Spitfire and Seafire it was another case of a superb land-based fighter being somewhat out of its element in the shipboard environment.

Chapter 39
North American B-25 Mitchell

The Mitchell medium bomber has been included in this book by special request, for it is one of the most popular aircraft with aviation enthusiasts and aircrew alike. There is also in the public mind a certain charisma about the Mitchell because of its fantastic attack on Japan in 1942. I assuredly belong to the multitude of pilots who enjoyed flying that great aeroplane.

The design of the XB-25 was approved on 10th September 1939 and the prototype flew on 19th August 1940. Since the B-25

was actually ordered off the drawing board, the XB-25 was really the first production aircraft. On test at Wright Field it exhibited poor directional stability in bombing runs, and excessive dihedral on the wings was suspected. Thus, although the XB-25 and the first nine production aircraft had wings with constant dihedral from roots to tips, subsequent aircraft had the outer wings re-rigged flat to give the gull-wing arrangement which became the distinctive characteristic of the Mitchell.

My first impression of the B-25 was how

The efficient Mitchell medium bomber.

functional and business-like it looked with its angular shape, large engines, tricycle undercarriage and its bristling guns. The aircraft I was going to fly on 20th August 1944 was a B-25J Mitchell III with a wing span of 67 ft 7 in, a length of 52 ft 11 in and a height of 15 ft 9 in. It was powered by two 1,700 hp Wright Cyclone R-2600-29 14-cylinder air-cooled radial engines with two-speed superchargers, driving three-bladed Hamilton Standard constant-speed fully-feathering airscrews.

This was the most widely produced version of the Mitchell in the role of precision bomber, with a glazed nose and a crew of six, including a bombardier. It had a formidable armament of 13×0.5 in machine-guns distributed in the nose, in a dorsal turret, in waist positions, and in the tail. Normally a 3,000 lb bomb load was carried, but a maximum of 4,000 lb was possible. The empty weight of the B-25J was 21,000 lb, the combat weight was 33,500 lb, and the maximum permissible weight was 41,800 lb.

The Mitchell's cockpit was entered by way of an underbelly hatch, and was surprisingly compact, with a fairly orderly layout and a reasonable view ahead. Starting up the mighty Cyclones made a distinct shudder of power run through the airframe, and they growled throatily when opened up. Taxying was made easy by the tricycle undercarriage, whose swivelling nosewheel had a shimmy damper and centering device, and by the powerful hydraulic brakes.

The take-off was perhaps the most exciting feature of the Mitchell, as the acceleration was so impressive. Before line-up the cowl gills were set one quarter open, the oil coolers open, all trimmers to the neutral position, and the flaps lowered 15–20 degrees. The engines were then opened up to about half power before the brakes were released and the full power of 44½ in Hg manifold pressure and 2,600 rpm was applied, resulting in a thunderous amount of noise. The elevators were very powerful in raising the nosewheel, and

unstick took place at 95 mph in a very short distance.

From lift-off the acceleration rapidly took the aircraft to its safety speed of 150 mph as the undercarriage and flaps were retracted. The initial rate of climb at 155 mph with 38 in Hg manifold pressure and 2,400 rpm was 1,110 ft/min, and stability was positive around all three axes.

In cruising flight the Mitchell was very pedestrian, having heavy but effective controls which needed a lot of trimming, and with very positive stability. These characteristics made it a good defensive gun platform and also a very steady bombing platform, so it deservedly earned itself a high reputation as a combat aeroplane.

The aircraft had mild stalling characteristics, and good asymmetric flight handling, although the rudders were very heavy and it was essential to trim out the foot loads as early as possible.

The B-25 was essentially an Air Force bomber, but the US Navy began taking an interest in it after the Doolittle raid on Tokyo in 1942, when 16 B-25Bs were craned on to the flight deck of the USS *Hornet*, ferried to within 625 miles of the coast of Japan and flown off on 18th April, led by Lt-Col. James Doolittle of the US Army Air Corps. The aircraft had been modified to increase the total internal fuel capacity to 950 Imperial gallons (1,141 US gallons), and had a special low-level bomb sight and an autopilot installed. Crews of five were carried, together with 3×500 lb bombs and an incendiary cluster, thus giving a take-off weight of 31,000 lb.

The B-25s met little ground fire and no enemy fighters, and all hit their assigned targets. Fifteen of the aircraft ran out of fuel and crashed in China, while the sixteenth landed in Soviet Siberia. Of the 80 flyers who took part in the raid, 9 lost their lives and 65 were back with the American forces before the war was over.

This episode impacted on both the US Navy and the British Royal Navy, and indeed the latter were already in 1944 planning a similar raid with Mosquitoes, following my successful deck-landing trials with the twin-engined bomber in March 1944.

The US Navy showed a great interest in the Mosquito deck-landing trials and let it be known that they were contemplating such trials with a B-25H, and sought my opinion of its suitability. The B-25H was essentially similar to the B-25J, so my comments on the latter would be valid for the H model.

On entering the circuit for landing the cowl gills were shut and the booster pumps switched on before reducing speed to 170 mph. The undercarriage was then lowered, giving a nose-down change of trim, which was counteracted by the nose-up change as the flaps were lowered at 150 mph. As the speed was further reduced the controls became significantly lighter and more effective, particularly the elevators. The approach speed for this first landing was 115 mph with touchdown at 100 mph. This was a very comfortable speed, and during the landing run the powerful elevators could hold the nosewheel off the ground to 60 mph.

It was obvious that the approach speed could be reduced further, and my next approach at 107 mph was still comfortable so I made a third at 100 mph with touchdown at 90 mph. Three more landings at this speed, simulating corrections for line and elevation, convinced me it would be practical to land the B-25H on an aircraft carrier. This view was endorsed by the RAE and conveyed to the US Navy.

In the event, the carrier USS *Shangri-La* conducted shipborne trials in November 1944 with a PBJ-1H, a Marine version of the B-25H, during which the aircraft made arrested landings and was catapulted off the ship.

In my opinion the Mitchell was probably the best and most versatile medium bomber of the Second World War, and this is substantiated by the fact that 9,816 were built, more than any other US twin-engined bomber. It not only served throughout the war with a number of Allied air forces, but continued to serve in many guises for a considerable postwar period. With a top speed of 303 mph at 13,000 ft it was not as fast as the Boston, but it carried more bombs and was more heavily armed for its defence. However, for sheer flying exhilaration I preferred the Boston.

The author landing a De Havilland Mosquito VI on the aircraft carrier HMS Indefatigable in March 1944.

Chapter 40
Percival Prentice

If ever there was an ugly duckling, it was the Percival Prentice. The P.40 Prentice 1 basic trainer was built to a specification which called for side-by-side seating with a third seat positioned centrally behind the two front seats. It was a low-wing monoplane with a fixed undercarriage and a large cockpit canopy stretching from the leading edge of the wing to just aft of the trailing edge. It was powered by a 250 hp de Havilland Gipsy Queen 32 driving a two-bladed variable-pitch metal airscrew. The wing span was a huge 46 ft, the length 31 ft 6½ in, the empty weight 3,232 lb and loaded weight of 4,350 lb.

I first flew the prototype Prentice, TV163, on 30th July 1946 at RAE Farnborough, and thereafter three more times in August to assess its handling qualities, which fell down badly on a great number of points.

Taxying was easy, with excellent view, good brakes and powerful rudder effect, and take-off was simple and straight-forward, but once into the cruise at 126 mph the troubles started to show up. Harmony of control was poor, with heavy elevators, moderately heavy ailerons, and very light rudder. Longitudinal stability was satisfactory, but stick force per 'g' was exceptionally high at 25 lb; laterally the aircraft was unstable, and although the rate of roll was acceptable, the forces to apply full aileron built up quite appreciably with increase in speed – 12 lb at 70 mph, 18 lb at 110 mph and 26 lb at 150 mph. The directional stability was very good, but the aircraft snaked directionally in rough air, making instrument flying a real chore.

For aerobatics the Prentice was a real old cow. Manoeuvres in the looping plane were cumbersome owing to the heavy elevators, and slow rolls were impossible to accomplish with any degree of accuracy, because the rudder seemed to lose effect on coming out of the inverted position and the nose could not be held up or kept straight.

The stalling characteristics were bad for a trainer, with little pre-stall warning buffet and a 30 degrees port wing drop. With the use of flaps, the pre-stall warning was a longitudinal oscillation followed by a sharp starboard wing drop.

For landing, the aircraft was overflapped and had a very nose-down attitude in an engine-off approach at 60 mph, so that a hefty pull was required to attain the attitude for a three-point landing. This overflapping made the baulked landing case with full flap and three crew quite critical.

This was a formidable list of defects for any aircraft, but was still more undesirable in an elementary trainer. In that condition the Prentice was obviously unfit for Service use, so was returned to Percival's with the RAE report, to undergo the inevitable modifications.

On 14th September 1946 I carried out a flight at Luton Airport on TV163, which had been considerably modified as follows: (i) increased rudder tab gearing, and rudder travel increased from 15 degrees to 25 degrees; (ii) elevator chord reduced by 3 in; (iii) new ailerons of increased span (about 15 in increase) with one-third percentage nose balance instead of round nose balance, and with aileron-tab gearing reduced to zero; (iv) flaps decreased in span by about 15 in.

In flight the rudder felt considerably heavier than before, but full movement on the pedals was applying only 50% rudder at 110 mph and 40% at 130 mph owing to

The ugly duckling Prentice.

stretch in the control cables. Directional stability and snaking were unaffected.

The elevators were slightly lighter, the stick force per 'g' having been reduced to 20 lb at 130 mph. Longitudinal stability was still satisfactory.

The ailerons had become heavier, the force to apply full stick now being 30 lb at 110 mph, but the rate of roll had improved. Lateral stability was now neutral.

The reduced flap area had resulted in a shallower gliding attitude, but the stick movement and force to effect a three-point landing was still too large for comfort.

Changes to all three control surfaces continued throughout the rest of 1946 on TV163 and all of 1947 on TV163, VN684 and VR193, and I made a series of flights both at Luton and Farnborough, during which the aircraft began to change shape noticeably in the rudder and elevators, while the wings acquired turned-up tips. The

handling did improve, but not to any significant degree, and a slow roll was still impossible to execute without loss of height and direction. This aerobatic manoeuvre is a good functional test of the effectiveness of all three controls, so it was obvious that the Prentice was never going to be a good primary trainer.

To add to the Prentice's troubles it had bad spinning characteristics, in that the spin was flat and could give an inexperienced student problems in recovery. So on 3rd March 1948 I began a new phase of tests aimed at solving this problem. The aircraft was prototype TV172 with the upturned wing-tips removed, a modified rudder, and a dorsal fin fitted. All of the tests were made with two crew, usually myself and an RAE scientific officer, and up to 12 spins were tried on each flight. The spins were made in each direction and using standard and non-standard methods of entry and recovery after the spin had stabilised. On this first test the results always gave an initial steep spin which became a flat spin with slow recovery (up to four turns) requiring a two-handed push on the stick.

For the second test, on 2nd April, the upturned wing-tips were still removed, the rudder area was reduced, extended and sharpened anti-spin strakes were fitted, and the dorsal fin was retained. The spin was still flat and the recovery still required a two-hand push on the stick, but the number of turns was reduced to three before recovery action took effect, so it was back to the drawing board.

For the third test, on 18th June, the fuselage was lengthened by 3 ft and the fin area increased. Still the spin became flat, but recovery could be effected in two turns, although the stick force continued to be high.

The fourth test, on 8th October, really saw a radical change to the Prentice with the introduction of VN684 complete with twin fins and rudders. In this case the spin flattened abruptly and the rotation was quite slow and oscillatory. Recovery could be made by the standard method or using rudder only in about one-and-a-half to two turns. Quite apart from having minimal effect on the spin characteristics, the rudders proved ineffective on take-off and in improving the slow roll shortcomings.

Time was running out in this spinning saga, so Percival settled on the version with the lengthened fuselage for production, and I did a final check on the pre-production model, TV172, on 16th December 1948. In my opinion the Prentice was still far from satisfactory for use as a Service trainer.

On 10th February 1949 I flew G-23-1, a production model for the Argentinian Air Force, to check the finalised spin characteristics. By this time I had spun the Prentice in 16 different conditions of airframe modification, so I was not expecting too much. I certainly was not disappointed.

Spins were made in both directions from 8,000 ft and photographed by cine camera from a Harvard flying at 7,000 ft. The spin, as usual, was two-staged. It was steep and fast though rather jerky for three turns after initiation, and then it flattened most markedly and at the same time the rate of rotation slowed up considerably. Throughout the entire spin the aileron tended to lock on in the pre-spin direction, and it required about 15 lb stick force to hold the stick neutral.

Recovery could not be effected on rudder alone, and the foot load was rather heavy, being about 70 lb. On pushing the stick forward the force built up rapidly until it became about 40 lb at neutral, and unless the stick was forced beyond this position no sign of recovery was apparent. However, when the stick was pushed well forward recovery was effected in two turns.

It was significant that during the first spin I took what I deemed to be normal recovery action after eight turns (three steep, five flat), and yet for the next six turns there was no effect whatsoever until I definitely forced the stick forward with a push that almost required two hands because of the poor leverage that could be exerted with the elbow well bent.

My inevitable conclusion was that this particular version of the Prentice displayed the worst characteristics I had experienced in the series of spin tests. The fact that the spin was two-stage was not in itself dangerous, but the control forces required to recover were too high for safety in an elementary trainer. However, this was the version released to the Services, and in my opinion it should never have got that far.

Chapter 41
Republic P-47D Thunderbolt

There can have been few more contradictory aeroplanes than the Republic Thunderbolt. It looked massive for a fighter, especially in comparison with the fine lines of the contemporary Spitfire, yet it had impressive performance. It was primarily a high-altitude escort fighter for Flying Fortress bombers in Europe, yet it had a lethal Achilles' heel in that role.

The Thunderbolt evolved from the Seversky P-35 and Republic P-43 Lancer, both designed by the Russian emigré engineer Alexander Kartveli. The first example of the Thunderbolt to fly was the XP-47B, which incorporated features based on information fed back from combat experience in Europe before America had entered the Second World War. In the main, these features involved increased firepower, increased fuel capacity, and increased protection for the pilot and fuel tanks.

Above all, the P-47 design was affected by the turbo supercharger system, the installation of which had to avoid creating drag. Kartveli solved this by burying the lengthy ducting and blower in a deep

The heavyweight Republic Thunderbolt fighter.

fuselage, and in spite of its complexity the supercharging system worked extremely well and proved relatively immune from combat damage. Fuel tanks and the ducts in the centre fuselage necessitated a high position for the pilot.

Other novel features on the XP-47B were a four-bladed propeller (the first time on a US production fighter), and telescopic pre-retracting undercarriage legs necessitated to give adequate ground clearance for the 12 ft diameter propeller. The wings carried 8×0.5 in belt-fed Browning machine-guns with the ammunition belts lying flush in spanwise channels outboard of the guns.

The XP-47B made its first flight on 6th May 1941 at a weight of 12,086 lb, the heaviest and largest single-seat fighter the US Army Air Corps had ever ordered. Its potential was demonstrated by the eventual achievement of a top speed of 412 mph at 25,800 ft, a service ceiling of 38,000 ft, and a rate of climb of 3,000 ft/min.

The production P-47Bs were only used for training in the USA, and the P-47C became the first combat version of the Thunderbolt. The engine of the C model was moved 8 in further forward, and the extra space ahead of the firewall was used to install a water injection system for the engine.

The P-47C effectively became fully operational in England on 8th April 1943, but did not have the range to escort the B-17 bombers more than about 200 miles. It was superseded by the P47-D, which began reaching the US squadrons in England in mid-1943, and the use of drop tanks increased the radius of action to 375 miles.

About the beginning of 1944 reports began reaching the RAE of Thunderbolts diving out of control from high-altitude combat, and eventually in March of that year a P-47D was seconded to RAE Farnborough from the US Eighth Air Force for investigation, since it was suspected that the cause was compressibility induced, and the RAE was at that time heavily involved in research in the transonic flight range. The aircraft was powered by a Pratt

& Whitney R-2800-59 Double Wasp 18-cylinder two-row air-cooled radial engine with water injection, rated at 2,000 hp at 33,000 ft, and 2,300 hp with water injection at 31,000 ft.

Although I had flown big and heavy fighters such as the Chance-Vought Corsair and Blackburn Firebrand, they had not looked as bulky as the Thunderbolt. Certainly the cockpit was very reminiscent of the Corsair, suitable for a modern fully kitted American football player. The view from the lofty position was not good dead ahead, but was otherwise fair. Starting up that mighty engine was simple, and it purred like a contented pussycat. It took quite a lot of power to get the juggernaut moving, but once rolling it was easy to taxy, although the nose had to be swung from side to side to allow view ahead.

The take-off was lengthy, but the climb surprisingly nimble, and on the way uphill I took the opportunity to check the stability, which was positive laterally and direction-ally, but neutral longitudinally. The controls were rather heavy for a fighter, especially the elevators, but they were all effective at climb and cruise speeds.

I did some general handling at 5,000 and 20,000 ft before going on up to 30,000 ft for a level speed run. It was obvious that this aeroplane was not at its best at low level, but came into its own at high altitude. With combat emergency power I computed that after a 3 min run the true air speed was 425 mph. The elevator trim tab position was noted for this run and similar runs at 35,000 and 25,000 ft.

Before the next flight a Machmeter was fitted to the aircraft, and as instructed I climbed to 35,000 ft, carried out a 2 min level run at full power and trimmed the aircraft before pushing over into a 30 degree dive. At Mach=0.72 the aircraft began to buffet slightly and pitch nose down, requiring a strong pull force to maintain the dive angle. At Mach=0.73 the buffeting increased severely and the nose-down pitch was so strong that it needed a full-blooded two-handed pull to keep the dive angle constant. I had to hang on grimly in this situation, unable to throttle back until Mach number decreased as altitude was lost. The pull-out was not effected until 8,000 ft. Analysis showed that a dive to M=0.74 would almost certainly be a 'graveyard dive'.

I have only subsequently experienced such severe compressibility nose-down pitch effects in two other aircraft, the Messerschmitt 163B and the Grumman F-8F Bearcat. Anyway, the RAE recommendation was to fit a dive recovery flap on the underside of the wing, which when activated would give a nose-up pitch to counter the compressibility nose-down pitch. This was eventually fitted to all Thunderbolt models.

In spite of its limitations in high speed dives, the Thunderbolt had a fine turn of speed in level flight, and an experimental version, the XP-47J powered by an R-2800-57 engine with a war emergency rating of 2,800 hp at 32,500 ft and considerable changes to the cooling system, achieved a speed of 507 mph at 34,450 ft on 5th August 1944, which was the highest known speed up to that time for a propeller-driven aircraft.

The Thunderbolt had a fairly short operational span of 2½ years, yet achieved some remarkable results. The USAAF claims that 7,067 enemy aircraft were destroyed by P-47s, almost equally divided between air combat and ground attack. Altogether 3,499 Thunderbolts were lost in combat, of which 824 were in air-to-air combat, giving a loss ratio of 1 to 4.6.

In all, 15,683 Thunderbolts were produced, a third of which were lost in combat or on non-operational flights. Certainly its record in training showed that it was not an easy aeroplane to fly to its limits, and it came as a particular shock to those pilots who found it replacing their Spitfires.

My own experience of the Thunderbolt was too short to make a thorough assessment of it, but I certainly remember it as one of the aircraft that made my adrenalin flow faster than usual.

The P-47D Thunderbolt with three auxiliary fuel tanks.

Chapter 42
Siebel Si 204D

I have a great affection for the Siebel 204D, as this eminently utilitarian aeroplane became my personal mode of transport when scouring the remnants of the German Third Reich for surviving examples of the more exotic aircraft of the lately demised Luftwaffe. Although hardly in the exotic class, the Siebel 204Ds which I liberated were in a class of their own on many counts, as I shall explain.

The Si 204D first appeared in Germany in 1942 and was principally produced in occupied France. It was a functional and at the same time good-looking aeroplane of all-metal structure with a single-spar wing and a dihedral tailplane with twin fins and rudders at its tips. The tailplane incidence was adjustable, and electrically-operated trim tabs were fitted. A crew of two and eight passengers could be carried, and besides transport duties the Si 204D was used for instrument, radio, radar and navigation training.

The aircraft was powered by two 600 hp Argus As 411 12-cylinder inverted Vee air-cooled engines driving two-bladed air-screws with pitch-changing vanes in front of the spinners. The fuel capacity was 240

My trusty Siebel 204D, a captured prize of war.

The Siebel 204D, a fine utility aeroplane.

Imperial gallons, the wing span was 69 ft 11¾ in, the length was 39 ft 2½ in, empty weight was 8,710 lb and loaded weight 12,348 lb.

The Si 204D had a beautiful cockpit with a fully glazed nose, which gave a perfect view such as can usually only be found in a helicopter. There were three separate systems for priming the engines, and three separate methods of starting them (one internal and two external), making it an ideal aeroplane for field operations. Certainly I took it to some very remote corners of postwar devastated Europe, and, carrying a German maintenance NCO and some jerry cans of fuel, managed to survive without difficulty in all sorts of weather and on all sorts of surfaces.

I transported many of Britain's top scientists on these air safaris, and only once nearly came unstuck. I had to take four eminent boffins to a deserted airstrip at Bad Oeyenhausen on 22nd August 1945, and on the approach at 100 ft, with wheels and flaps down, I saw a tractor suddenly head across the single tarmac runway. I had no option but to open up to go round again, when suddenly the port engine began acting up and misfiring badly. The runway was very short and with rising ground ahead, but at 50 ft over the threshold I realised that the point of no return had been passed. The airfield was being cultivated and there were haystacks dotted all around, so I eased off the corrective rudder I had applied, let the Siebel drift on to the grass and headed it full tilt into a haystack. The windmilling airscrews acted as threshing machines and we decelerated smartly but without damage. The offending farmer fled in his tractor, leaving my illustrious passengers to defluff the aircraft while my mechanic and I removed the oiled-up spark plugs and cleaned them with the aid of our passengers' pipe-cleaners and nail files before taxying clear.

The Si 204D was really a viceless aeroplane to handle, with inherently good stability around all three axes and good harmony of control. It was very well equipped for its tasks, and the later models I flew had an autopilot fitted. Like all German aircraft of that era it was a mass of electrics, with extensive circuit breaker panels, and all very reliable. However, the one thing the Germans never got right was wheel brakes, and the Siebel was no exception.

Performance was ideal for its functional tasks, with a rate of climb of 1,000ft/min, a maximum speed of 228 mph at 9,500 ft, a cruise speed of 211 mph, a service ceiling of 24,600 ft, and a range of 1,118 miles.

Ten captured examples of the Si 204D passed through our hands at RAE Farnborough and were extensively used without any real problems, and all the pilots who flew the type spoke highly of its efficiency.

Chapter 43
Taylorcraft Auster V

Light aircraft were not the run-of-the-mill stuff we normally dealt with at RAE Farnborough, but in this case it was not the aeroplane but the idea behind the experiment that attracted me.

A special three-rail track had been prepared at the RAE to test the possibility of flying off light 'grasshopper' liaison aircraft such as the Auster from tank-landing ships (LSTs) fitted with such a track. A Mk.V version of the Auster was chosen for the experiment, its serial number being TJ537.

The Auster was basically an American designed cabin monoplane built in England under licence from the Taylorcraft Aircraft Corporation, and progressively modified to meet Service requirements, particularly by the incorporation of wing flaps and the installation of higher-powered engines.

The Auster V had the same redesigned fuselage as the Mk.IV, with greatly improved rearward view owing to an extended area of Perspex in the upper fuselage aft of the wing. It was also the first model to have a full blind-flying instrument panel and a standard elevator

The Auster V in the start position on the LST track.

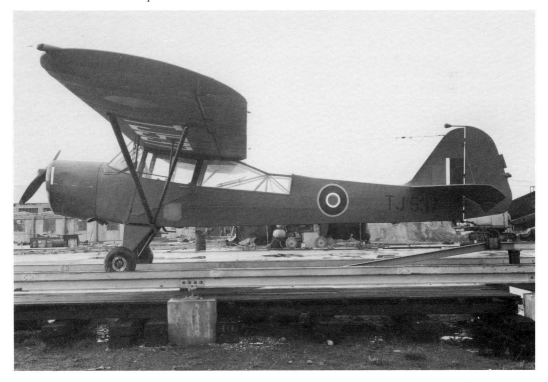

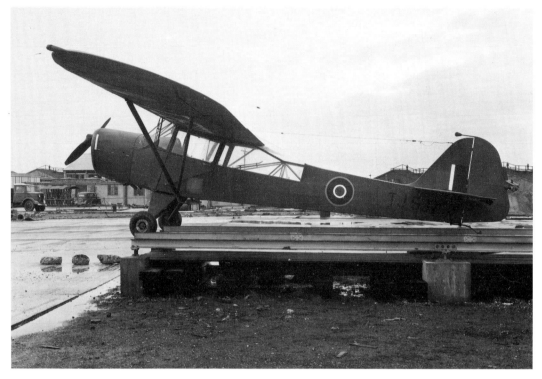

The Auster's tail wheel in the middle of dipping to increase lift on the take-off run.

trimmer. The powerplant was a 130 hp Lycoming O-290 4-cylinder horizontally-opposed air-cooled engine. The all-up weight for the tests was 1,300 lb with only myself aboard as pilot.

As a preliminary to the main tests it was necessary to establish the stalling speeds at the test weight. The clean stall, with flaps up, was 36 mph; with flaps at TAKE-OFF it was 34 mph; with flaps at LANDING it was a lowly 30 mph; and at EMERGENCY LANDING it was a rather indeterminate figure just below 30 mph.

The next step was a series of short take-offs from the main runway at the three flap settings, with photographic coverage for analysis. From these it was established that the flap position for optimum lift:drag ratio was LANDING, the TAKE-OFF position giving too little lift and EMERGENCY LANDING giving too much drag.

The RAE track for this experiment was 167 ft long and mounted on concrete pillars 2 ft 9 in above ground level. The Auster's main wheels were fitted into the two outboard guide rails, and the tailwheel mounted on a small bogey running on the centre rail, which was raised 14½ in above the level of the other two rails so that the aircraft was almost in level flight attitude (9° incidence on the mainplane, or 4° nose down from ground attitude).

This tail-up position was limited by the airscrew clearance available, and under the circumstances gave the best possible attitude for acceleration along the 150 ft of run available (the length of aircraft from main wheels to tailwheel was 17 ft). The normal ground attitude of the aircraft gave 13 degrees of incidence on the mainplane.

At the starting end of the track two collapsible chocks were incorporated in the main guide rails, and the tailwheel was

The Auster's tail wheel in the full dip position to give maximum lift at the end of the LST track.

held fixed in its trolley. On receiving the appropriate signal from the pilot after run-up, the safety pin was withdrawn from the chocks, which were collapsed by an external lever to allow the aircraft to start its take-off run.

The only other mechanical action involved in take-off was the behaviour of the tailwheel bogey. Its guide rail gradually started to dip at 15 ft from the end of the track and descended down a ramp to a level 10½ in below that of the main wheels, so that the aircraft changed its mainplane incidence sharply to 16 degrees (3 degrees nose-up from ground attitude), and then the tailwheel was released from its trolley simultaneously with the main wheels leaving the track, this release being made positive by the trolley hitting a buffer at the end of the ramp.

After a few trial launches it was found that the optimum result was obtained by setting the elevator trimmer three-quarters of its travel tail-heavy, lowering the flaps to the LANDING position, and checking there was sufficient friction damping applied to the throttle.

On the final engine run-up against the chocks I checked the engine revs. and then transferred my right hand from the central throttle to the stick, holding up my left hand as a 'ready-to-go' signal. I then gave the 'go' signal by dropping my left hand, while holding the stick three-quarters of the way fully back and applying a touch of right rudder. The stick position aided the ultimate unstick by increasing the angle of attack of the aircraft beyond that given it by the tailwheel rail as it left the track, and although the angle of climb away was sharp, there was not enough elevator travel available to stall the Auster under full power conditions with landing flap applied.

In spite of the apparently automatic take-off action of the scheme, it was found in practice that windspeed and aircraft weight affected the take-off run so critically that they had to be correlated to calculate the required take-off distance, but by using the technique already described the pilot could decrease the distance by about 30 per cent.

Such a gain was of great import because the tank landing craft was not able to guarantee more than a 10 knot windspeed along the track from its own headway in dead calm conditions, though it did provide a drop of 15 to 20 ft between the end of the track and sea level, and this would have been used to the fullest advantage to transform the aircraft from a partially stalled state into a fully airborne state – a technique familiar to naval pilots operating from the flight decks of aircraft carriers.

My general impression of the Auster V was that it was not in the same class as the German Fieseler Storch with regard to take-off and landing performance or general slow flying, and in fact I found the British machine a bit of a handful in really bumpy weather. Be that as it may, the little Auster would certainly have provided a welcome 'eye in the sky' for assault troops when operated from LSTs fitted with the special track as tested successfully at the RAE.